Foreword

By the early 1990s many firms in the construction industry had put in place quality management systems to BS 5750 (now BS EN ISO 9000) and achieved third-party certification. A range of publications was available on quality management in construction, including a significant series of reports from CIRIA. There was also a well-developed market in consultancy providing advice and assistance.

However, a vigorous debate continued on the benefits (or otherwise) of quality management systems to BS 5750, and of the certification procedure. Much of the discussion was on the basis of personal views and experience. There was thus a clear need to collect objective and representative evidence of the practical outcome of applying BS 5750 to the construction industry, and thereby provide reliable information for those considering certification or wishing to review an existing quality management system. In 1992 CIRIA launched a project to meet this need.

Following usual CIRIA practice, a contract to carry out the research and write the report was tendered in competition, and won by Bucknall Austin Plc in association with Liverpool John Moores University. The report was initially drafted by Mr D Hugill and Mr A Grice, and developed and edited by Mr M Ward, all of Bucknall Austin Plc. The project was overseen by a widely representative Steering Group, who provided extensive comment on successive drafts of the report. It comprised:

Mr B Philpott (Chairman)	–	Building Design Partnership
Mr P Challenger succeeded by Mr R G Sutcliffe	–	AMEC Civil Engineering Ltd
Mr M C Clavell	–	Management Consultant, representing Christiani and Nielsen Ltd
Mr C J Fox succeeded by Mr A R Wittering	–	Department of Transport, latterly Highways Agency
Mr C N Jones	–	Higgs and Hill Construction Holdings Ltd
Mr C R D Moss	–	L G Mouchel and Partners Ltd
Mr D Salter	–	Salmon Speed Architects
Mr F Smith	–	Abbey National Homes Ltd, also representing the Institute of Clerks of Works
Mr J Smythe	–	Trafalgar House Construction (Major Projects) Ltd
Mr C F J Ward	–	Thames Water Utilities

CIRIA's Research Manager for the project was Mr A Jackson-Robbins.

The project was funded by CIRIA's Core Programme and the Department of the Environment. CIRIA and Bucknall Austin Plc are grateful for help given to this project not only by the members of the Steering Group, but also the many individuals and organisations who were consulted in the course of the field research. In accordance with undertakings given to these contributors, they are not identified.

Contents

Figures

Tables

Abbreviations

BCSA	British Constructional Steelwork Association Ltd (see SCQAS)
BS 5750	BS EN ISO 9000 (formerly BS 5750) Quality Systems
BS	British Standard
BSIQA	BSI Quality Assurance
CARES	Certification Authority for Reinforcing Steel
CICS	Ceramic Industry Certification Scheme Ltd
CQA	Construction Quality Assurance
LRQA	Lloyds Register Quality Assurance Ltd
NACCB	National Accreditation Council for Certification Bodies (see UKAS)
Nr	Number
QA	Quality Assurance
QMS	Quality Management System
QSRMC	The Quality Scheme for Ready Mixed Concrete
SCQAS	Steel Construction QA Scheme Ltd (formerly BCSA)
TQM	Total Quality Management
TRADA	Timber Research and Development Association
UKAS	UK Accreditation Series (formerly NACCB)
YARSLEY	Yarsley Quality Assured Firms Ltd

Glossary

Quality Management System (QMS)	BS 4778 defines a QMS as the organisation structure, responsibilities, activities, resources, and events that together provide organised procedures and methods of implementation to ensure the capability of the organisation to meet quality requirements.
Internal Auditing	A systematic and independent examination to determine whether quality activities and related results comply with planned arrangements and whether these arrangements are implemented effectively and are suitable to achieve objectives.
Certification	The process by which a firm's quality system is assessed by an independent, recognised assessor. If successful, the firm is then qualified for inclusion on the Register of Quality Assessed United Kingdom Companies.
Management Review	A review and evaluation of the QMS by appropriate members of a firm's management to ensure its continuing suitability and effectiveness.
Supplier	Any firm from which goods or services are purchased.
QA Representative	The staff member having responsibility for the operation and maintenance of the QMS.
Investors In People (IIP)	A national standard which aims to help organisations improve performance through a planned approach to setting and communicating business goals and developing people to meet these goals.
Total Quality Management (TQM)	BS 7850 defines TQM as a management philosophy and company practices that aim to harness the human and material resources of an organisation in the most effective way to achieve the objectives of the organisation.

Executive summary

INTRODUCTION

This report presents the findings from a survey of experiences of BS 5750 within the construction industry. A total of 35 firms were interviewed from across the industry to determine their experiences of installing a Quality Management Systems (QMS) to BS 5750, together with the experiences of 30 clients of these firms. In addition, the survey sought the experiences of seven firms who indicated that they operated an alternative QMS to BS 5750.

MAIN FINDINGS

The following summarises the main findings of the report:

- **Implementation strategy:** Most firms (20 of the 35) sought to increase business opportunities and improve the firm's profile. Only two firms installed their QMS because of client pressure. Generally, firms did not have a clear strategy and only eight had a budget. This may explain why 23 firms employed a consultant to assist with the installation of their QMS.

- **QMS design and implementation:** Most firms included 75% or more of their business activities within their QMS and appointed a senior member of staff as the Quality Assurance (QA) Representative. Twenty-three firms involved their employees in the development of the documentation, approximately 70% of which took the form of new procedures.

  On average, the installation of the QMS took 29 months, of which 14 months related to the design of the system. The QA Representative and employees' time were the major cost items: third-party certification costs ranged from £1000 for a firm of 12 employees, to £36 000 for a firm with 600 employees.

- **Maintenance of a Quality Management System:** All 35 firms found internal auditing beneficial and improvements to the business were made by 17 firms. Generally, management reviews were carried out either once or twice a year. Only 16 firms, however, were able to improve their system. The interviews identified that a number of firms appeared to lack a fundamental understanding of BS 5750.

  On average, third-party audits were carried out twice per year and some 21 firms found the visits worthwhile. Twenty firms reported that they had also been subject to a second party audit from a large client, suggesting that certification alone may not meet all client requirements.

- **Perceptions of BS 5750 Quality Management Systems feedback from certified firms:** Whilst experiences differed amongst firms, some improvements were gained in most areas of the business, in particular company image and information flow. Most firms felt that paperwork had risen significantly, although some believed this was necessary and had improved management control. Overall, firms were of the opinion that their products, services, management controls had improved, although the level of improvement was slightly lower in professional service firms.

- **Purchaser/Client attitudes towards supplier and project quality:** Most clients had good working relationships with their suppliers. Whilst they believed that suppliers should demonstrate a commitment to quality, only 15 stated that the achievement of BS 5750 was taken into account during selection.

  Generally, improvements in performance following certification ranged from 40% to 87%. Indeed, the level of improvements, in terms of confidence of meeting requirements, the time taken to deal with problems and the overall image of firms, was considered to be greater in the opinion of the clients than their suppliers.

- **Other responses to market requirements for quality management:** seven firms from different sectors of the industry completed a questionnaire regarding their alternative approach to quality management. Of the seven firms, five claimed to follow a Total Quality Management (TQM) programme whilst two managed quality as part of the day-to-day management of their businesses.

  Whilst no clear conclusions can be drawn from a sample of firms as small as seven, the evidence suggests that these firms are probably not managing quality in a defined and measurable way. The advantages that a TQM approach can bring are, however, enormous: indeed, many firms seek to build on their QMS and incorporate the human development aspects of the TQM approach.

MAIN CONCLUSIONS

The survey shows that, overall, firms from certain sectors believe they have made significant improvements to key areas of their business as a result of implementing a QMS to BS 5750 and gaining certification. Firms' clients have also seen significant improvements to the products and services supplied to them by these firms. The evidence obtained from both the firms themselves and their clients suggests that, generally, BS 5750 is appropriate for these sectors of the construction industry.

Whilst firms have seen improvements in many areas of their business, the survey has shown that time and again the level of improvement is perceived to have been at a lower level than expected (see Section 4). The reasons for this are as a result of a combination of two major factors:

1. In some cases, for example with regard to sales levels, firms' expectations may have been too high. Clients indicated that BS 5750 is only one of several criteria for supplier selection. These issues are addressed in Section 4 and Section 5.

2. Internal auditing and management review are key tools with which firms ensure that their QMS remains effective and develops with the changing business. A review of these processes, as discussed in Section 3, suggests that many of the firms interviewed, whilst meeting the requirements of the Standard, did not gain the full benefits that these processes can bring. This may be because some firms have been unable to allocate sufficient time and resources towards the development of their system, whilst others may not have a full understanding of BS 5750. A review of the case studies, which provide key data regarding the experiences of each firm, shows that some firms consider Corrective Action, Inspection and Testing, Control of Nonconforming Product and Design Control to be the least important sections of BS 5750. These are, in fact, key areas of the Standard.

THE WAY FORWARD

This report suggests, through the experiences of the firms participating in the survey and their clients, that implementing a QMS to BS 5750 can be an effective way of managing quality within firms in the construction industry. A number of issues, however, could be considered to assist firms:

1. Firms should work more closely with their suppliers and take an active interest in their quality management systems to ensure that their requirements for quality are met.

2. BSI should consider a review providing additional guidance notes:
   - to make it easier for firms to understand how the Standard relates to their business.
   - to provide further guidance on internal auditing and, in particular, Management Review.

3. With the recent growth in certification bodies firms need to consider carefully which certification body is right for them. The UK Accreditation Service (UKAS) should continue to ensure that certification standards are maintained.

Introduction

BACKGROUND

BS 5750 was first published in 1979. Since that time there has been much debate on how appropriate this Standard is to the construction industry, and particularly on:

- the effectiveness of quality management systems to BS 5750, and

- the value of third-party certification.

Many of the views expressed have been personal or based on limited experience. Thus there has been a clear need for a survey of experiences of BS 5750 that would be both objective and representative, from which reliable lessons might be learned. The CIRIA research project carried out for this report sought to meet that need.

OBJECTIVE

The objective of the research programme was to assess the implementation of BS 5750 in the construction industry, against the background of arguments both for and against its use. In particular, the researchers sought to identify, evaluate and draw conclusions from:

- the benefits obtained by firms who had achieved certification, their customers and the industry

- the time and resources required to design and implement a QMS and achieve certification

- the annual cost of maintaining the QMS

- any drawbacks or disappointments.

The purpose of this report is to present and comment on the findings, and thereby assist those who are:

- considering installation and certification of a QMS TO BS 5750

- wishing to review the operation of an existing QMS.

This advice is intended to be of value to those responsible for overall policy decisions, typically directors and partners, as well as designated 'quality managers'.

The report also considers the implications for the future development of quality management systems in the UK construction industry.

FIELD RESEARCH

The survey of experiences was carried out throughout 1993, in three successive phases.

First phase: Firms providing products or services

The purpose of the first phase of research was to capture the experiences of firms representing a cross-section of the supply side of the industry. A limited number (35) were studied in relative depth, in preference to seeking a larger sample that would have given greater statistical reliability, but at a more superficial level. To help ensure that the experience quoted was well-founded, as far as possible firms were selected that had achieved certification prior to January 1991 from a body accredited by the NACCB. An implication of this was that these firms were arguably pioneers in the field; it was necessary to take this into account in weighing their experiences.

Five firms were identified in each of seven sectors of the industry, as set out in Table 1.

Table 1 *Sector of industry surveyed*

Professional services	Architects
	Quantity Surveyors
	Consulting Engineers
Contractors	Main Contractors
	Specialist and Trade Contractors
Manufacturers and suppliers	Construction Product Manufacturers
	Construction Material Suppliers

The firms within each sector were selected as far as possible to provide a spread in terms of:

• geographical location

• size (by number of employees)

• accredited body used for certification.

Of the firms selected, two, a consulting engineering practice and a main contractor, had gained certification after 1991, in June and February 1992 respectively. Accordingly, some of the benefits which become apparent in the longer term, will not have manifested themselves at the time of the research.

Information was obtained through structured interviews, using a detailed, 41-page 'interview assessment'. To provide an internal cross-check, up to three individuals were interviewed in each firm, at different levels, covering both those 'managing' and those 'being managed', as follows:

• senior management/quality representative

• middle manager

• operative/technician.

In total 87 people were interviewed.

The interview assessment was structured under seven headings. Information was sought from the senior manager under all seven headings, and from the other interviewees under three key headings only, as indicated in Table 2.

Table 2 *Topics covered in structured interviews*

Heading	Senior Management	Middle Management	Operative/ Technician
General information about the firm	✓		
General information about the QMS	✓		
Experience of designing and installing the QMS	✓	✓	✓
Experience of maintaining the QMS	✓	✓	✓
Observed benefits and drawbacks	✓	✓	✓
Observed implications for performance of projects	✓		
Other information	✓		

The essence of the interview was to seek to identify:

- the effects expected by the firm from implementing a QMS to BS 5750 and achieving certification

- in comparison, the effects actually experienced.

Second phase: The firms' clients

The purpose of the second phase was to establish the experiences of clients who had, as far as possible, purchased goods and services from firms interviewed in phase one, both before and after certification.

Following the identification of 30 such client firms, a senior manager was invited to complete a questionnaire. This document was structured into four major sections:

- general information about the firm

- the approach to supplier quality

- observed implications for the performance of projects

- other information.

Third Phase: Firms operating alternative quality systems to BS 5750

The purpose of this final phase was to establish the experiences of firms which had implemented an alternative quality management system to BS 5750, in order to compare their achievements and experiences with those of the firms covered in phase one. Seven such firms were identified.

A senior manager from each firm was invited to complete a questionnaire, comprising six major sections:

- general information about the firm

- why the firm decided against BS 5750

- the firm's quality management strategy

- the elements of BS 5750 included in the firm's QMS

- observed benefits and drawbacks

- other information.

STRUCTURE OF THE REPORTS

The study is published as two parts:

SP132. Report of the key findings, and discussion of the issues arising. (This publication).

PR32. Selected interview material from firms studied in depth, presented as 'case studies'. published as Project Report 32. These place the issues discussed here in their proper context, and will enable readers to explore and evaluate other issues of interest to them.

This report is presented in sections that broadly follow the order in which information was obtained in the research. It is intended to be read as a whole. Each section, however, is set out to allow the reader easy access to particular topics. Key words identifying the content of each section are set out in Table 3.

Table 3 *Key topics and issues covered by the report*

Section	Key topics	Issues covered
1	Implementation strategy	Objectives; methods adopted in practice.
2	Design and implementation of a QMS	Getting started; the QA Manager; scope; documentation preparation; extent of changes required to existing procedures; resources required to implement a QMS; planning for certification.
3	Maintenance of a Quality Management System	Auditing; management review; resources required to maintain a QMS.
4	Perceptions of a QMS to BS 5750: feedback from certified firms	Methodology; benefits and drawbacks of a QMS to BS 5750; overall impressions of the effect of BS 5750 upon the business.
5	Purchaser/Client attitudes towards supplier and project quality	Attitudes, requirements and experiences; implications on construction projects; perceived importance of BS 5750, by type of business.
6	Other responses to market requirements for quality management	Objectives; methodologies; results claimed.
7	Conclusions	Conclusions; overall impressions of BS 5750 in the construction industry; lessons learned; the way forward.

1 Implementation strategy

1.1 INTRODUCTION

This section of the report deals with the objectives that firms sought to achieve from a Quality Management System (QMS) and describes the implementation strategies adopted in pursuit of certification to BS 5750. Respondents were asked to state their objectives for pursuing certification and to describe their strategy for the design of their QMS, with reference to such matters as management of the design and implementation process, resources, training and documentation development.

1.2 OBJECTIVES

The firms which participated in this survey were each asked to describe the key objectives regarding their decision to implement a QMS. The objectives of each firm and the benefits expected from implementing a QMS are provided in the case studies.

Thirty of the 35 firms stated that they wished to improve the standing of their business in the market place and/or increase opportunities for increased business. Of these, only two firms, a quantity surveyor's practice and a main contractor, confirmed that they had installed their QMS in response to client pressure. A further three, however, aware of increasing public sector interest in the quality systems of suppliers, sought to increase opportunities in this sector.

The remaining five firms sought to improve the management controls within their businesses: two of these also sought to improve productivity.

Of the 30 firms wishing to gain a marketing advantage, 14 also sought to improve their levels of productivity and efficiency. A further five expected to improve their management controls. A total of five firms expected to gain improvements in all three areas.

The above summarises the objectives of the 35 firms and the benefits they expected at the outset. There are, however, some interesting differences between the seven sectors considered in this survey. These differences can be seen by examining the case studies. Generally:

- Architects sought not only to gain marketing advantages but also to improve management controls and productivity.

- Specialist and trade contractors, quantity surveyors and product manufacturers sought mainly marketing objectives.

- Consulting engineers' objectives were mixed. Four of the five interviewed, however, wished to improve their management controls.

- The objectives of main contractors and material suppliers focused both on marketing and productivity issues.

1.3 METHODS ADOPTED IN PRACTICE

The firms from each of the seven sectors covered by this survey varied significantly both in size and management style. Their experiences regarding their approach towards implementing a QMS to BS 5750 were equally varied. Discussions with respondents revealed two significant features:

1. The majority of firms had no clear strategy in place prior to commencement.

   This is evidenced by the responses to a request to describe the strategy for the overall design of their QMS. Most responses, as can be seen in the case studies, provided only an overview of the methodology actually adopted. Several firms, perhaps not surprisingly, were unable to describe their methodology for the implementation of their QMS due to the time that had elapsed and/or changes in personnel since certification.

2. Only eight firms had established a budget for the introduction of their QMS.

   When planning the implementation of a QMS it can often be difficult, at the outset, to assess how long the process will take and cost. Most firms had little knowledge of the process and sought guidance from a consultant regarding the most appropriate manner in which to design and implement their QMS.

The methods adopted by each of the 35 firms in regard to the introduction of a QMS are provided in the case studies. The key issues considered were:

- Whether or not to use a quality consultant?

  Twenty-three of the 35 participants used a quality consultant to assist with the development and/or implementation of their QMS, spending between £1000 and £55 000 (for a company with 550 employees). Of these, two thirds spent less than £4500, often under the DTi 'Enterprise Initiative' grant aid scheme, designed to help small to medium-sized enterprises develop their businesses. Those with higher consultants' fees tended to be larger companies.

  This shows that most of the firms who were interviewed during the survey felt a need to have access to professional advice in the form of someone experienced in interpreting and implementing BS 5750. In other words, most firms 'buy in' the expertise. A prime reason for this is that many prefer to 'buy in' short-term professional experience, rather than invest in the lengthy training process that would be necessary were they to use in-house resources.

- Who should be appointed in the role(s) of QA Representative (see Section 2.2)?

  Most organisations appointed an in-house senior manager at an early stage to develop the documentation.

  This demonstrates that most businesses realised at a very early stage that the development and implementation of a QMS needs to be project managed by a senior manager. This manager should be able to devote time to the project, have excellent communication skills at all levels, in order to encourage input from all staff, and have a voice at Board level.

- What should be the scope of certification?

  When a firm seeks certification to BS 5750 it must define which business activities within its QMS are to be certified. All but three firms attained certification for over 75% of their business activities.

Whilst a firm can attain certification for only specific activities, it should consider carefully what implications this may have on the business, especially in terms of credibility in the marketplace.

- What procedures would be needed under a QMS?

When planning the implementation of a QMS, it is important to analyse what procedures will be needed, taking into account the areas of the business to be covered by the QMS, and the degree of interaction with any existing systems, such as Health and Safety. Once these have been determined, it is possible to identify which areas are already covered by the firm's existing procedures and provide a rough indication of the work required to develop a documented set of procedures.

Every organisation included in the survey introduced amended or new procedures as part of their QMS. On average, at least 70% of procedures had to be amended or developed from scratch (see Section 2.5). This suggests that companies considering the implementation of a QMS to BS 5750 should not underestimate the extent to which new procedures will need to be developed.

- The extent to which employees would participate in the design and implementation of the system?

As can be seen in Table 5, (see Section 2.4.1) 20 firms involved their employees in the development of their procedures. A further three actively sought the views of employees prior to implementing procedures formally. The majority of firms held in-house training sessions, seminars or discussions.

This is a clear indication that the firms surveyed felt it important to involve people at all levels in the development and implementation of the QMS.

- What relationship an individual office/site would have with the centre in a multi-location organisation?

Of the 21 organisations having more than one certified location:

seven had a single certificate to cover all locations
eleven had separate certificates for each location
one had separate certificates for each operating division regardless of location
two had regional certificates covering a number of locations.

This reflects the fact that there are various ways to obtain certification for an organisation operating from more than one site (see Section 2.8).

1.4 CONCLUSIONS

The research has shown that most firms covered by this survey decided to install a QMS to BS 5750 and gain certification in order to improve their profile in the industry or increase business. Only two firms decided to install their QMS as a result of client pressure.

Evidence suggests that it is possible to embark on a project to install a QMS and obtain certification to BS 5750 without a clear strategy. The majority of firms, however, employed the services of a consultant: the results of the survey indicate that appropriate methodologies were implemented by most firms. Indeed, 32 of the 35 firms participating in the survey achieved certification at the first attempt. A lack of a clear strategy or methodology will presumably mean that it is more difficult to ascertain progress and measure achievements. It may also mean:

- the implementation process may take longer, cost more and require extensive reviews
- it may be difficult to ensure that the people in the business are fully involved in the process and in the most effective manner
- a high risk of installing an inappropriate system.

The time taken by firms to implement their quality management systems, the people involved in their development and the effectiveness of the documentation produced is discussed in the following two sections.

2 Design and implementation of a QMS

2.1 THE FIRST MOVES TOWARDS INSTALLING A QMS

As discussed in Section 1, a firm may have a number of reasons for deciding to introduce a QMS. Whatever the firm's objectives, the process of designing and implementing a QMS to BS 5750 requires all personnel in the business to focus on:

- understanding and meeting customer needs

- understanding the business processes

- investing time and effort in preventing errors.

To achieve this, it is important that senior management are fully committed and lead the drive for quality. Any fundamental change in the philosophy and culture of the organisation must be initiated by, and have the continued close involvement of, senior management. To gain maximum benefit from the introduction of a QMS, it is important that senior management maintain their involvement and their interest throughout the project. In initiating the move towards a QMS the management must:

- ensure that the aims and objectives are clearly understood by everyone in the business

- demonstrate on a daily basis their own commitment to these aims

- encourage the employees to become actively involved in the development of an effective QMS.

In practice, the introduction of a QMS is normally spearheaded by a senior member of the management team. Indeed, the research data shows that in all of the seven sectors covered by the survey, very senior management were involved at the initiation or inception stage of the process. In over 80% of the firms in the survey, the move towards a QMS was set in motion by either a Director or a Partner. This indicates that they understand that the decision to implement a formal QMS affects the very heart of the business, and therefore needs senior level involvement and commitment.

2.2 THE QUALITY ASSURANCE REPRESENTATIVE

BS 5750 requires the appointment of a 'Management Representative' (usually referred to as the Quality Assurance Representative or QA Representative) who is to have 'defined authority and responsibility for ensuring that the requirements of this International Standard are implemented and maintained'.

The person responsible for this role within each of the 35 firms participating in the survey is shown in the case studies. In every case the position is held by a senior member of the management and demonstrates that all firms saw the role of the QA Representative as an important management function. Unfortunately, it is possible for a firm to see this role as purely administrative, merely ensuring that the functional requirements of each section are complied with. Such firms rarely gain the full benefit from their QMS.

With the right person in the post, the QA Representative will go beyond these routine administrative duties and actively solicit feedback from employees, suppliers and customers that enables the QMS to be constantly updated and improved. Under these circumstances, the QMS becomes a 'live' system, an integral part of the business and a way of thinking for its employees.

During the survey respondents were asked to state their selection criteria in appointing the QA Representative and whether or not the individual was recruited from outside the firm. Generally speaking, the QA Representative was an existing member of staff. Only seven firms recruited from outside.

The criteria considered by each firm in selecting the person for the position of QA Representative are given in the case studies, a broad range of skills, knowledge and experience being listed. The most frequently cited personal requirements of the QA Representative are shown in Table 4.

Table 4 *Attributes of a Quality Manager*

Personal attributes	Percentage of firms citing attributes
1. Knowledge of and commitment to QA	37%
2. Credibility of individual	34%
3. Technical knowledge (of product/ service/process)	29%
4. Knowledge of firm	26%
5. Good communication skills	26%

2.3 SCOPE OF CERTIFICATION

When a firm applies for BS 5750 certification, it specifies which of its activities are to be included in the registration. For example, if a firm is involved in both road building and plant hire, it may choose to exclude the plant hire business from the scope of its BS 5750 certification.

Most firms participating in the survey chose to include all of their business activities in their scope of certification. Only 12 of the participating firms carried out additional business activities not covered by their scope:

- Architects   1
- Quantity surveyors   3
- Consulting engineers   3
- Main contractors   3
- Speciality and trade contractors   1
- Construction product manufacturers   1
- Construction materials suppliers   0

All but three of these are larger organisations that employ more than 100 people and have a diverse range of products or services. Thirty-two firms stated that the scope of their certification covers more than 75% of their business.

The scope of each firm's registration is described in the case studies. As would be expected, those organisations involved with design (of products or services) were generally certified to BS 5750: Part 1. Those organisations involved only with contracting and production were certified to BS 5750: Part 2. Three of the construction materials suppliers were certified under a stockist scheme, designed specifically for stockists and merchants. One of the quantity surveyors was certified to Part 2 of the Standard, whilst offering similar services to the other firms in this sector (who were certified under Part 1). More notably, six of the ten main contractors and specialist trade contractors were certified to Part 1 of the Standard.

2.4 QMS DOCUMENTATION

2.4.1 Drafting the QMS documentation

Table 5 below summarises the personnel involved with the development of the documented procedures required for BS 5750. In 27 of the firms studied, the documentation was drafted by the QA Representative, assisted either by other employees or a consultant.

Table 5 *Preparation of QMS Documentation*

Document preparation	Number of firms
QA Representative assisted by employees	12
QA Representative assisted by employees and Consultant	6
QA Representative assisted by Consultant	7
QA Representative assisted by Consultant and Directors	1
QA Representative assisted by Directors/Partners	1
Senior Manager assisted by employees	2
Senior Manager assisted by employees and Consultant	2
Senior Manager assisted by Consultant/QA Representative	2
QA Representative	1
Senior Manager	1

Table 5 shows that 22 firms involved their employees in the development of their documented procedures. This enabled staff to contribute to the process and develop a sense of 'ownership' of the QMS.

2.4.2 The Scope of QMS Documentation

Most businesses pursuing BS 5750 certification within the construction industry will already have management systems in place for other aspects of the business, especially for matters such as Health and Safety. As a result, it is important to determine how the QMS documentation should relate to these other systems. Discussions with the firms participating in the survey revealed that 23 firms had incorporated a significant number of regulatory requirements within their documentation. These are listed in Appendix 2.

In order to satisfy the requirements of BS 5750, a firm must document its quality procedures to show how, for each section of the standard, the firm meets requirements. There are some activities within the business, such as marketing, finance and information technology which could fall outside mandatory requirements. Many firms, however, choose to include additional areas of the business to gain full benefit throughout, as well as involving all employees. Seventeen of the 35 firms included such non-mandatory areas within their QMS. Three of these saw this extension as a start towards Total Quality Management (TQM). Two firms have developed the training requirements of BS 5750 as part of their achievement of 'Investors in People'.

2.4.3 Reviewing the QMS documentation

Table 6 summarises the wide range of approaches among the firms surveyed to the important task of reviewing documented procedures prior to implementation.

Table 6 *Review of QMS Documentation*

Documentation review	Number of firms
QA Representative assisted by employees	11
QA Representative assisted by employees and Consultant	5
QA Representative assisted by Consultant	4
QA Representative assisted by Consultant and Directors	1
QA Representative assisted by Directors/Partners	3
Senior Manager assisted by employees	2
Senior Manager assisted by employees and Consultant	2
Senior Manager assisted by Consultant/QA Representative	2
QA Representative	1
Senior Manager/Director/Partner	4

A total of 20 firms involved their employees in reviewing the QMS documented procedures. By involving staff fully these firms ensured that the procedures were 'approved' by the staff which would use them. Again, this encourages employees to become actively involved in the 'management' of quality. In the remaining 15 firms, the documentation was reviewed by senior staff, and in four of these, by a senior member of staff in isolation. In such firms, the opportunity to involve staff in the quality management process has been lost.

Respondents were also asked to comment on the structure and level of their documentation. Provided that the QMS documentation is controlled, firms have a high degree of freedom regarding the structure of the documentation. Discussions with respondents confirmed a high degree of variation between the participating firms. Most interviewees were of the opinion that the initial documentation was too extensive and too detailed, resulting in the QMS becoming inflexible, and firms have reduced the amount of paperwork since certification, making their system more practical. This suggests that there may be a tendency for firms initially to develop procedures that are too detailed, resulting in documentation which may become inflexible and impractical.

2.5 THE EXTENT OF CHANGE REQUIRED TO EXISTING PROCEDURES

The survey measured the extent to which the installation and certification of a QMS required the development of procedures beyond those incorporated in previous management systems. The firms covered by this study were asked to indicate, as a percentage, the proportion of procedures in their QMS which were:

- unamended from previous documented procedures

- a development of previous procedures (some amendments of documented procedures or formulation of non-documented procedures)

- entirely new.

Figure 1 shows the average percentages by industry sector.

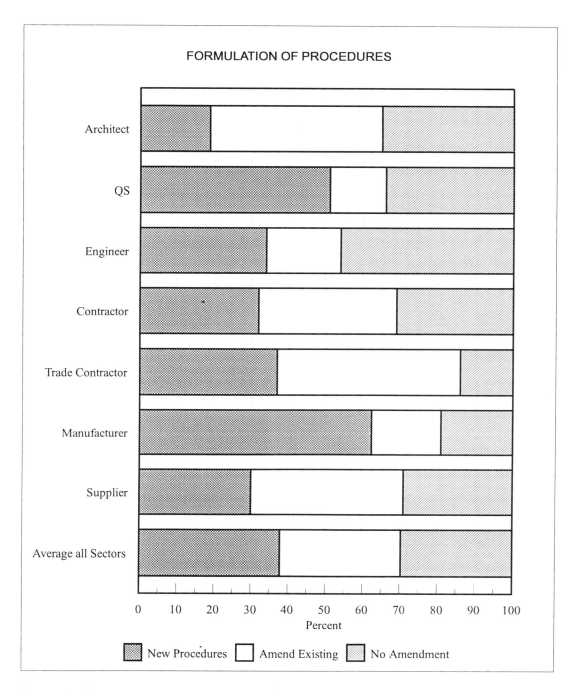

Figure 1 *Changes to management procedures*

Overall, 70% of all procedures were developed from scratch or amended from existing procedures. This confirms that firms should not underestimate the degree to which they will need to revise existing procedures and develop entirely new ones.

As can be seen from the figure, there is a significant variation in the experiences of each sector. Furthermore, as can be seen in the case studies, there are also significant variations within each sector.

2.6 THE PHASES AND TIMESCALES OF SYSTEM DESIGN AND IMPLEMENTATION

Four key dates were recorded for each organisation, marking three phases of system development as set out in Table 7.

Table 7 *Phases of system development*

Key dates		Phase
1. First consideration of formal QMS	2. Starting work on system	Consideration
2. Starting work on system ...	3. System applied to working processes	System design
3. The system applied to working processes	4. Date of certification	Implementation

The average timescales recorded for each sector are shown in Figure 2. The average timescales for the 29 firms which provided responses were:

- Consideration   6 months
- System design   14 months
- Implementation   9 months
- Total   29 months

(Note: The responses of the firm of consulting engineers represented in case study number 11 have been excluded from the analysis as the firm reported that it took 108 months (nine years) to gain certification. This length of time is exceptional and the firm has been excluded to prevent a serious distortion of the overall analysis).

The times taken to gain certification are provided in the cases studies. These show that there is a significant variation between respondents within each sector. Table 8 illustrates the timescales reported by firms of different sizes.

Table 8 *Average timescales, in months, for achieving certification*

Number of employees	Number of firms	Consideration	System design	Implementation	Total
6−50	12	2.9	8.1	9.0	20.0
51−100	9	8.5	14.8	7.2	30.5
101−250	4	5.2	8.7	15.5	29.5
251 and over	9	6.7	26.0	12.5	45.2

The analysis above shows a very general trend, namely, that the time taken to design and implement a QMS increases with size of firm.

It is suggested that, due to lack of knowledge and lack of market pressure, these early pioneers took longer than organisations who have more recently embarked upon the route to BS 5750 certification.

Only four of the participating firms achieved certification in less than 12 months following initial consideration, the shortest period being eight months and the longest period 46 months, excluding the exceptional 84 months taken by the one consulting engineering practice.

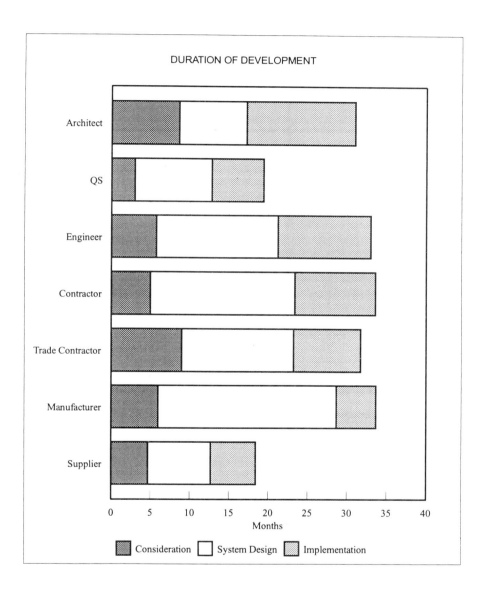

Figure 2 *Average timescales for achieving certification*

2.7 RESOURCES REQUIRED TO IMPLEMENT A QUALITY MANAGEMENT SYSTEM

2.7.1 Establishing a budget

The greatest cost in the development of a QMS is normally that associated with the time spent by employees in developing and maintaining the system. A number of firms (27) which did not establish a specific budget prior to starting work believed that staff would have to find the time, in addition to their normal duties, to be involved in the development of their QMS. With 'external' costs, such as those associated with certification expected to be modest, these firms saw no benefit in developing a budget.

In the eight organisations which did establish a cost budget, five met cost targets and the remaining three deviated from their budgets by less than 25%. This suggests that these firms found establishing a budget to be beneficial in that not only were they able to assess the cost of gaining certification, but they were also able to make necessary financial provisions.

2.7.2 Resources Required

The major cost items, excluding employees time, were the quality consultant's fees and the initial third-party assessment costs. The costs of these two items, together with firms' estimates of the time spent by the QA Representative and by other employees, are shown in Table 9.

Incidental costs for such items as stationery, labelling, printing, etc., which are important considerations when introducing a QMS in some types of business, were quoted by five firms in the range £200 to £2000. External training courses were used by only two firms, amounting to £400 and £1000 respectively.

Table 9 illustrates that the human resources utilised by firms in their drive to implement a QMS varies significantly between firms within each sector and between sectors.

By applying any reasonable cost factor to the staff time quoted, it is evident in all cases that cost of staff time was the major resource implication. As might be expected, this cost rises according to the size of firm. This is illustrated in Table 10.

2.8 PLANNING FOR CERTIFICATION

Following the implementation of their QMS, firms considered which third-party certification body would be chosen. Whilst BSI is responsible for the issue and control of the Standard, there are over thirty organisations in the UK accredited to certify a QMS to BS 5750. Firms, therefore, had to consider carefully which certification body was the most appropriate for their business.

The diversity of certification bodies that were employed was one of the criteria used for the selection of the firms that participated in this survey. The nine certification bodies employed are shown in Table 11. Five of the certification bodies were of a specialist nature, for example QSRMC, which specialises in the certification of ready-mix concrete suppliers. The remaining four certification bodies, such as BSI Quality Assurance, cover a range of activities within the construction industry.

Table 9 *Resources required to design and implement a QMS*

Nature of business	Case study	No. of employees	Cost of Consultant (£000)	Time of QA representative man weeks	Staff time man weeks	Cert. fee (£000)
Architect	01	12	3	42	104	4
	02	n/a	3	52	30	4.3
	03	100	1.2	47	21	1.1
	04	208	40	152	80	5
	05	40	4.5	4	10	3
Quantity Surveyor	06	14	n/a	4	2.5	4
	07	100	3	25	20	2
	08	550	55	52	300	n/a
	09	8	23	10	3	2
	10	11	1.8	16	16	2
Consulting Engineer	11	490	n/a	52	500	n/a
	12	160	1	10	10	3
	13	15	n/a	15	n/a	n/a
	14	200	n/a	52	10	n/a
	15	55	n/a	n/a	n/a	n/a
Main Contractor	16	150	2.5	50	60	3.5
	17	700	0	70	4	5
	18	249	10	30	45	10
	19	600	2.5	100	18	3.5
	20	41	0	20	84	3.1
Specialist and Trade Contractor	21	362	0	25	60	8.5
	22	50	4.5	8	2	3
	23	600	32	26	146	36
	24	100	4	15	10	3
	25	80	0	150	10	n/a
Construction Product Manufacturer	26	450	0	52	n/a	n/a
	27	15	3	6	0	n/a
	28	300	n/a	n/a	n/a	n/a
	29	76	6.75	14	7	n/a
	30	80	0	52	39	1
Construction Materials Supplier	31	65	3.05	35	0	2.5
	32	12	2.5	12	3	1
	33	31	3	15	5	4.0
	34	56	1	36	50	3.3
	35	6	0	13	0	0.5/ plant

Table 10 *Staff time required up to certification*

Number of employees	Number of firms	QA Manager (man weeks)		Total staff (man weeks)	
		Range	Average	Range	Average
6−50	12	4−42	14	0−104	19
51−100	9	14−150	47	0−50	20
101−250	4	10−152	53	10−80	49
251 and over	9	25−100	60	4−500	148

Table 11 *Certification bodies used*

Cert. Body/Sector	Prof. Services			Contractors		Manufacturers & Suppliers	
	Arch	QS	Engr	Main	Trade	Manufacturers	Suppliers
BCSA	—	—	—	—	1	—	—
BSIQA	4	3	2	3	1	2	2
CARES	—	—	—	—	—	1	—
CICS	—	—	—	—	—	1	—
CQA	—	—	2	1	—	—	—
LRQA	1	1	—	1	—	—	—
QSRMC		—	—		—	—	1
TRADA		—	—		1	1	1
YARSLEY		1	1		2		1

The certification bodies used by the firms participating in the survey were all accredited by the UKAS for their type of business, and were chosen on three main criteria:

- the standing of the certification body in the marketplace

- the cost structure with regard to the initial certification and the ongoing surveillance costs

- knowledge of the firm's type of business.

The survey did not solicit comment on the policies or performance of the certification bodies.

2.9 CONCLUSIONS

A review of how the firms designed and implemented their QMS suggests that, overall, they saw the need to manage the process from the top, with a senior manager taking responsibility for the QA Representative's role. Most firms sought certification for 75% or more of their business activities and, by involving their employees (22 of the 35 firms interviewed) in the drafting and review of the documentation prior to implementation, they were able to ensure that staff had input into both their style and content. This process can be an important team-building tool which can lay the foundations for improving morale throughout the business.

The time taken to install the QMS and gain certification varied significantly between firms. The average time taken was 29 months: six months consideration, 14 months system design and nine months implementation. The major cost items were those associated with the QA Representative's and employees' time, ranging from a total of 33 man weeks for firms of 6 to 50 employees to 208 man weeks for firms of over 250 employees. Third-party certification fees ranged from £1000 for a material supplier of 12 employees to £36 000 for a specialist and trade contractor with 600 employees.

3 Maintenance of a Quality Management System

3.1 INTRODUCTION

A good Quality Management System should develop as time passes in order to remain effective and meet the changing needs of the business. This section of the report deals with the methods which firms participating in the survey use for the ongoing management and development of their QMS.

The main parts of this process are:

- Quality System auditing: a systematic and independent examination of the QMS to determine whether the activities are carried out as stated in the documentation, and to ensure that the requirements of BS 5750 are met.

- Management Review: the process of looking at the effectiveness of the QMS and identifying any necessary changes in the context of the changing needs of the business.

Both of these processes are requirements of BS 5750.

3.2 AUDITING

3.2.1 Types and Objectives of Auditing

There are three principal types of audits which the organisation can undertake:

1. A quality system audit carried out by a firm on its own QMS — first-party, or internal, auditing.

2. An audit carried out on the firm's QMS by one of its clients, or an audit carried out by the firm on a supplier — second-party auditing.

3. An audit carried out by an independent body to certify compliance with BS 5750 — third-party auditing.

The auditing process has three principal objectives:

- to determine whether or not the organisation is complying with the procedures defined in its QMS

- to assess whether the QMS procedures are effective

- to provide information for Management Review.

3.2.2 Experience of internal quality auditing

The research in this area solicited feedback from three levels of each of the 35 businesses that participated in the survey, these being senior management, middle management and operational staff.

The benefits and difficulties experienced with respect to internal quality auditing, as reported by the senior managers/QA Representatives, are listed in the case studies in Project Report 32. Their experiences may be summarised as follows:

All firms reported that they had found internal quality audits to be beneficial. The most common reported benefits fell into four main categories:

- ensuring that procedures are implemented

- identifying problems and areas for development

- improving checking and information flow, leading to improved communications and management confidence

- improving staff awareness of quality and, in one case, morale through recognition of work done.

Seventeen firms reported that they were able to improve their QMS as a result of information obtained from internal auditing.

Sixteen firms reported no drawbacks arising from the auditing process. The major problems experienced by the remaining 19 were:

- time to carry out auditing (12)

- disruption caused by auditing (4)

- increased costs as a result of auditing (4)

- the manner in which auditing is carried out (1)

Some firms reported problems in more than one area.

Many firms, when first considering whether to implement a QMS, perceive the auditing process to be an administrative burden, an overhead that produces intangible results. The survey data demonstrates that the internal auditing process for 17 firms provided significant benefits and useful information which enabled the QMS to be consistently improved.

3.2.3 Experience of second party auditing

Twenty of the organisations had been audited by a client:

- Architects   1
- Quantity surveyors   3
- Consulting engineers   4
- Main contractors   1
- Specialist and trade contractors   3
- Construction product manufacturers 3
- Construction material suppliers   5

Five organisations (primarily in the product manufacturer and material supplier categories) had been audited by more than five different clients.

The high proportion of firms which had undergone second-party audits (approaching two thirds) suggests that certification to BS 5750 may not provide certain clients, in particular large public and private concerns, sufficient confidence that their supplier's QMS meets all their requirements. In some cases, second-party audits are carried out in specific areas of the business where the supplier's QMS is expected to go beyond the requirements of BS 5750 alone. This suggests that for some firms, BS 5750 is seen as a framework on which other systems can be developed.

3.2.4 Experience of third-party auditing

The frequency of third party audits undertaken by firms ranged from once to four times per year. Most, however, are audited twice a year. The full results are given in Table 12.

Table 12 *Frequency of third-party auditing*

Sector	Frequency per annum			
	1	2	3	4
Architects	1	3	1	–
Quantity Surveyors	–	5	–	–
Consulting Engineers	1	4	–	–
Main Contractors	1	2	–	2
Specialist and Trade Contractors	–	4	1	–
Construction Product Manufacturers	1	4	–	–
Construction Materials Suppliers	1	4	–	–

The auditing process, by its very nature, relates to the state of the business at a specific time. Furthermore, only a relatively small proportion of the firm's activities are normally audited at any one time. Accordingly, certification bodies will normally audit the firm more frequently during the first two years of registration than thereafter. This explains why some organisations reported receiving up to four third-party audits during the initial years after certification.

Of the 35 firms, 21 believed third-party auditing had been beneficial to their QMS and a further seven responses were neutral. The nature and limited frequency of third-party audits, however, suggests that firms should not rely on their certification body in regard to the optimum development of their QMS. The principal role of the certification body is to determine whether, in practice, the firm's quality management system meets the requirements of BS 5750.

3.3 MANAGEMENT REVIEW

3.3.1 Objectives

The purpose of the management review process is to examine the effectiveness of the QMS with respect to the ongoing needs of the business. The management review will consider information from a variety of sources, in order to ensure that the QMS continues to meet the needs of the business, its customers and BS 5750.

The review takes the form of a formal meeting and may take place annually, for example as part of the business planning process, or more frequently, depending on the style of management of the firm. Third-party certification bodies normally require a review to be carried out not less than once per year.

In determining how the management review process is managed firms considered:

- Who should attend the meetings?

- How often management review meetings would be held?

- What would be on the agenda?

The research sought to establish the method by which firms managed their review process and considered the frequency of the management review, the attendees and the agenda for the review meeting, together with the changes which arose from the review process.

3.3.2 Frequency and attendees

The frequency of reviews carried out by firms varied considerably. The full results are tabulated in Table 13.

Table 13 *Frequency of Management Reviews*

Construction sector	Frequency per annum					
	1	2	4	6	9	12
Architects	3	1	–	–	1	–
Quantity Surveyors	2	–	–	1	–	2
Consulting Engineers	3	2	–	–	–	–
Main Contractors	3	1	–	1	–	–
Specialist and Trade Contractors	1	3	1	–	–	–
Construction Product Manufacturers	1	1	–	–	–	3
Construction Materials Suppliers	3	1	–	1	–	–

The individuals attending these reviews, with very few exceptions were representatives or members of senior management. This suggests that, generally, management see the review of their QMS as an important management consideration, and not simply to comply with the requirements of the BS 5750 standard.

The variation in frequency of management review meetings reflects the different styles of management within the firms participating in the survey. The majority, however (over 70%), review their system either on a six-monthly or annual basis.

3.3.3 Review agenda

The items covered during management review meetings are provided in the case studies in Project Report 32. The subjects considered varied greatly between the 35 firms, and cannot, therefore, be presented on a sector-by-sector basis in a way which will be meaningful. The major subject areas stated by respondents are as follows:

- audit programme, reports and corrective actions (25)

- certification body matters (8)

- complaints (12)

- review of QMS documentation (22)

- staff reviews and training (7)

- supplier and subcontractor performance (4)

- design and contract reviews (4)

- quality records (1)

- revisions to statutory requirements (1)

- quality plans and other forms (2)

The above analysis of the subject areas covered by firms during their review meetings suggests that very few firms have considered all aspects of their QMS during the review process. This would suggest that there remains significant scope for further improvement in the majority of firms.

3.3.4 Changes arising from the management review

Senior managers/QA Representatives were asked about the changes which their firms had made to their QMS as a result of the management review process. Firms' experiences were varied but can be summarised as follows:

- working methods revised or improved (8)

- changes, improvements or introduction of customer complaints procedures (4)

- parts, or whole QMS, rewritten to be less bureaucratic, more practical and user friendly (4)

- extension of scope of QMS (3)

- approach or frequency of internal auditing changed (3)

- computer operations updated (2)

The number of firms which made significant improvements to their QMS, as shown above, is relatively low. This must, to some extent, suggest that the review of some firms' QMS could be significantly improved. There could be a number of reasons why not more firms have been able to improve their system. One factor could be the degree of understanding of BS 5750 that actually exists within the firm.

Respondents were asked to state, in their opinion, the most and least important sections of BS 5750: responses are recorded in the cases studies. The following summarises those sections of BS 5750 which firms considered to be least important to their business:

- management responsibility (2)

- quality system (1)

- design control (1)

- document control (3)

- purchasing (12)

- purchaser supplied product (13)

- product identification and traceability (8)

- process control (3)

- inspection and testing (5)

- inspection, measuring and test equipment (19)

- inspection and test status (13)

- control of nonconforming product (7)

- corrective action (3)

- handling, storage, packaging and delivery (10)

- quality records (5)

- servicing (4)

- statistical techniques (14)

- training (1)

These views suggest that in many firms there was not a full understanding of BS 5750. It is unlikely that such firms will attain all the benefits that operating a QMS to BS 5750 can bring.

3.4 RESOURCES REQUIRED TO MAINTAIN A QUALITY MANAGEMENT SYSTEM

The resources invested annually by the participating organisations in maintaining their certified QMS are summarised in Table 14.

Only two firms, both professional organisations, employed a consultant to assist with the upkeep/development of their QMS. The process was, generally, managed in house.

Third-party certification body annual fees varied from £500 to £4000 with one large organisation incurring an annual fee of £10 000.

Table 15 summarises the annual resources employed by firms, categorised by size, together with the annual cost of third-party certification.

Table 14 *Resources used annually to maintain a QMS*

Nature of business	Case study	No. of employees	Time of QA manager	Staff time	Cert. fee
Architect	01	12	21	3	2
	02	n/a	36	2	n/a
	03	100	10	1	1.5
	04	208	52	n/a	1.5
	05	40	2.5	8.5	n/a
Quantity Surveyor	06	14	3	1	1.3
	07	100	3	12	0.5
	08	550	5		n/a
	09	8	2	n/a	1.75
	10	11	4.5	0	1.4
				0.5	
Consulting Engineers	11	490	n/a	n/a	n/a
	12	160	52	n/a	n/a
	13	15	5	5	n/a
	14	200	13	3	1.2
	15	0	n/a	n/a	n/a
		55			
Main Contractors	16	150	20	42	2
	17	700	50		3.5
	18	249	n/a	2	n/a
	19	600	52	5	1
	20	41	5	7	1.55
				3	
Specialist and Trade Contractors	21	362	10	11	2.1
	22	50	5		1.5
	23	600	26	0	10
	24	100	52	0	1
	25	80	52	10	4
				4	
				78	
Construction Product Manufacturer	26	450	40	n/a	3
	27	15	26	0	0.8
	28	300	52	5	n/a
	29	76	26	3	0.9
	30	80	47	29	1.5
Construction Materials Suppliers	31	65	3	2	1.4/plant
	32	12	3	2	1.4
	33	31	9	2	n/a
	34	56	2	12	1
	35	6	13	0	0.5/plant

Table 15 *Resources used annually to maintain a QMS, by size*

Size of firms by number of employees	Sample number of firms	QA Rep. man weeks		Total staff man weeks		Certificate fee
		Range	Average	Range	Average	Average
6–50	12	2–26	8	0–9	3	£1,500
51–100	9	2–52	24	1–104	30	£1,500
101–250	4	20–52	41	5–42	24	£1,750
251 and over	9	5–52	31	2–11	5	£3,500

These results reveal two important considerations:

Firstly, the annual cost of third-party certification for firms with less than 250 employees is between £1500 and £1750. However it should be noted that with the increasing numbers of certification bodies fee structures are becoming more competitive.

Secondly, there appears to be no direct correlation between the size of the firm and the resources required. This demonstrates the different approaches that these firms adopted for the ongoing management of their QMS. Overall, however, firms of between six and 250 employees should expect to utilise between eight and 30 weeks of the QA Representative's time supported by up to 25 weeks of other employees' time.

3.5 CONCLUSIONS

The internal auditing and management review processes are fundamental to the effective development of the QMS within any business. Only 17 of the 35 firms interviewed, however, were able to improve their system as a result of either internal auditing or management review. Consideration of the agenda of firms for their management review meeting suggests that many firms considered only the minimum requirements of BS 5750, as discussed in Section 3.3.3. Such firms are unlikely to gain maximum benefit from operating a QMS to BS 5750.

The interviews with respondents also suggest that some firms, as noted in Section 3.3.4, may not have a full understanding of BS 5750: for example 12 firms believed that purchasing, a major section of BS 5750, was not important. Similarly, seven firms believed that control of non-conforming product was unimportant. Both these issues are key elements of BS 5750.

Overall, the impression is left that most firms interviewed could make significant improvements to their QMS: firstly, through gaining a better understanding of how the standard relates to their business; secondly, by considering a wider agenda for the management review process; and thirdly, by considering how the qms can be better managed and interfaced with other systems so as to produce the benefits required by the business.

4 Perceptions of Quality Management Systems to BS 5750: feedback from certified firms

4.1 INTRODUCTION

This section of the report addresses the perceptions of the firms that participated in the study of the benefits from operating their QMS and, where applicable, any drawbacks. Each firm was asked to summarise their experiences in a number of areas, and to outline the extent to which these had matched their original expectations.

4.2 METHODOLOGY

A separate interview was conducted with a senior manager, a middle manager and an operative or technician from each firm, during which their views were sought regarding the benefits gained by the business as a result of achieving certification. The interviews sought to establish both the extent to which firms' had achieved their original objectives for gaining certification, and also the benefits gained in other areas of the business. The specific areas focused upon were:

- company image
- production process
- costs
- planning and management control
- morale
- general management
- customer/client relationships.

A series of statements concerning each of the above areas was put to each respondent who was asked to consider both the benefits the firm had expected to achieve at the outset and those actually achieved as a result of gaining certification to BS 5750. The test statements used are listed in Table 16.

Table 16 *Criteria to measure the benefits of a QMS*

Area of impact	Test statement
	Achieving Certification to BS 5750 has:
Company Image	1. Enhanced the firm's image.
Production Process	2. Improved productivity throughout the firm.
	3. Improved information flow.
	4. Reduced the time it takes to deal with queries.
	5. Clarified responsibilities.
	6. Reduced the amount of paperwork.
Costs	7. Reduced administration costs.
	8. Achieved savings through a reduction in errors/failures.
	9. Achieved savings through a reduction in remedial work.
Planning and Control	10. Increased accuracy in predicting future activities.
	11. Improved control of resources.
	12. Increased certainty of achieving deadlines.
	13. Given greater confidence that targets will be achieved.
Morale	14. Improved personal job satisfaction.
	15. Improved job satisfaction generally within the firm.
General Management	16. Improved the identification of management issues.
	17. Improved operational matters – your projects/products.
	18. Reduced management attention required for routine matters.
	19. Reduced the amount of crisis management.
Customer/Client Relationships	20. Increased client/customer satisfaction.
	21. Increased the number of opportunities in the marketplace.
	22. Increased sales.
	23. Increased repeat business.

4.3 THE BENEFITS AND DRAWBACKS OF A QMS TO BS 5750

In order to illustrate the comparison between the benefits expected and those actually experienced by respondents, a summary of the average responses by senior managers/QA Representatives, for each sector, is provided in graph form. The individual responses, shown in the case studies, illustrate a variety of experiences not only across industry sectors but also between firms operating in the same sector. One firm, case study number 20, exhibited a particularly negative view regarding their experiences with BS 5750. It is useful, therefore, to consider the overall sector experiences in the light of individual responses.

In general terms the responses of both middle managers and operatives/technicians reflected those of the senior management. Where this is not the case, appropriate explanation is provided.

4.3.1 Company image

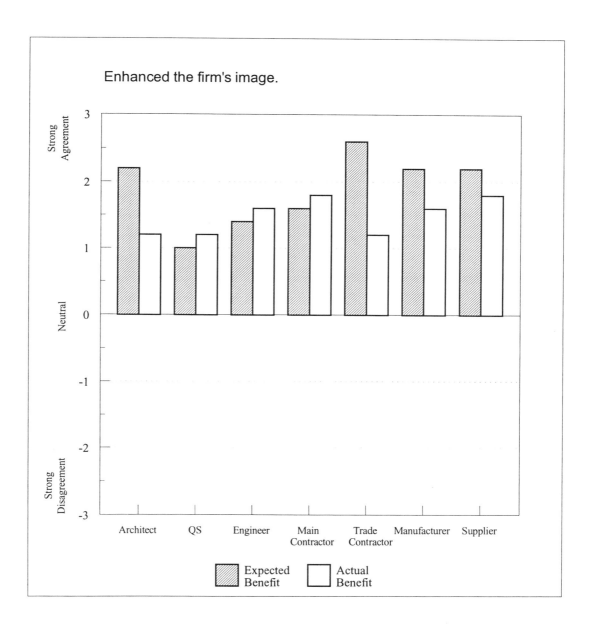

Figure 3 *Effect of QMS to BS 5750 upon firm's image*

A major objective of attaining certification for many firms was to increase the profile of their firm in the marketplace. It is not surprising, therefore, that firms expected significant improvements in this area. Quantity surveyors, consulting engineers and main contractors, however, had more modest expectations than the remaining sectors.

All respondents reported that in their view the image of their firm had improved as a result of gaining certification, but, with the exception of quantity surveyors, consulting engineers and main contractors, the degree of enhancement was generally less than expected.

4.3.2 Production process

There are five indicators that reflect the effect of BS 5750 on the production process. These are shown in Figures 4 to 8.

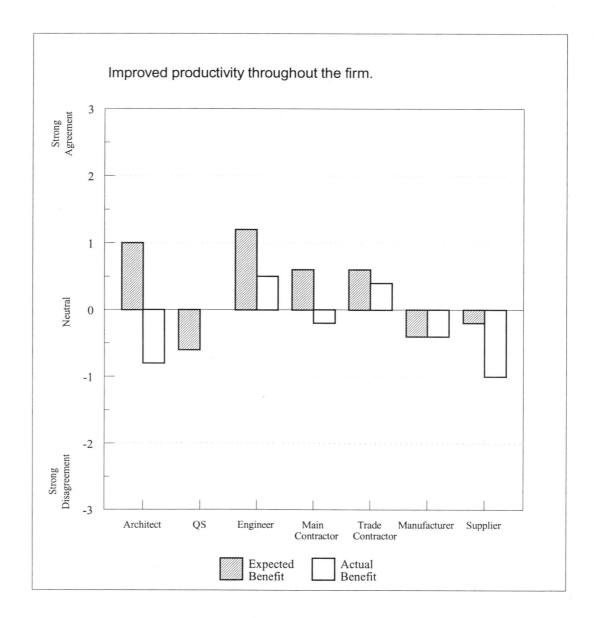

Figure 4 *Effect of QMS to BS 5750 upon productivity*

Whilst there were differences between the sectors, there were no high expectations of BS 5750 improving productivity. The architects, consulting engineers, main contractors and trade contractors expected some improvements in productivity whilst the quantity surveyors, product manufacturers and material suppliers had no expectations that introducing a QMS to BS 5750 would yield significant improvements.

With the exception of quantity surveyors, the perceived benefits have been slightly lower than expected. However, respondents from three architects, three material suppliers and one main contractor perceived the benefits gained to be lower than expected.

The 'middle managers' participating in the survey indicated general agreement with their senior managers. The more junior employees, however, generally thought that improvements had either been in line with, or slightly better than, expectations.

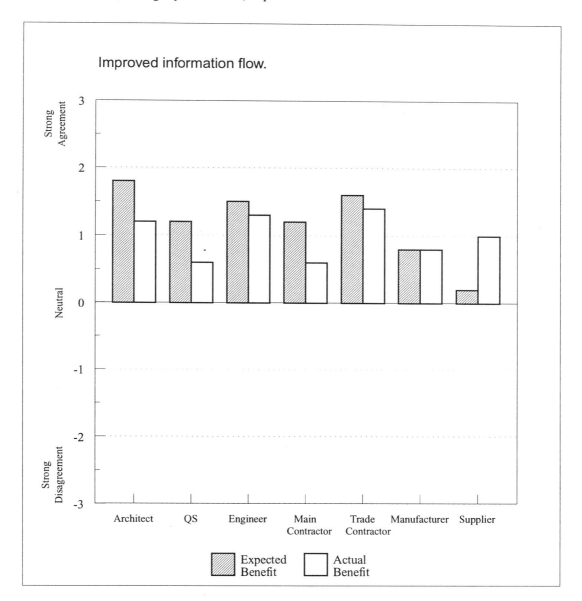

Figure 5 *Effect of QMS to BS 5750 upon information flow*

Firms in all sectors expected benefits in this area, although product manufacturers and material suppliers had slightly lower expectations than firms from other sectors.

Improvements in the flow of information were experienced by all sectors, in particular the material suppliers, where improvements were greater than expected. Only five firms (case studies 04, 20, 22, 28 and 33) believed that there had not been significant improvements.

'Middle' managers and operatives/technicians also believed that information flow had improved. Quantity surveyors at both 'middle' management and technician level believed that the improvements had been higher than those perceived by their senior counterparts. Technicians/Operatives from the consulting engineer and main contractor sectors perceived improvements to have been at a higher level than both senior and 'middle' management.

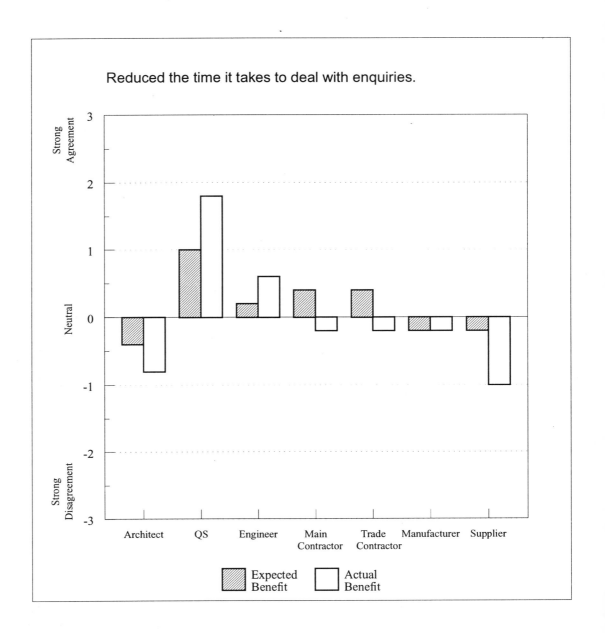

Figure 6 *Effect of QMS to BS 5750 upon dealing with queries*

Excepting the quantity surveyors, the firms surveyed anticipated that installing a QMS to BS 5750 would have only a marginal impact in this area.

Generally, the benefits experienced were in line with expectations, although the quantity surveyors and the consulting engineers saw better than expected improvements, whilst four out of five respondents from the material suppliers sector claimed that improvements had been less than expected. A further seven firms (case studies 04, 05, 15, 20, 24, 27 and 28) indicated that the level of improvement had been lower than expected.

Both 'middle' managers and operatives/technicians concurred with their senior managers that there had been only a marginal improvement in the time to deal with problems. However, respondents from the main contractors sector, at both levels, believed that the level of improvement had been marginally higher than expected. The operatives/technicians from the material suppliers sector also held the same view.

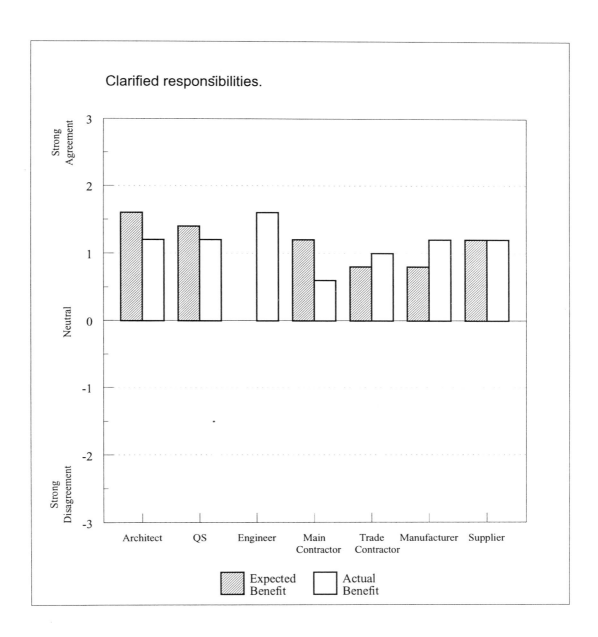

Figure 7 *Effect of QMS to BS 5750 upon clarification of responsibilities*

Apart from the consulting engineers, who had no strong views either way, all sectors expected their QMS to clarify responsibilities.

Firms' experiences show that implementing a QMS to BS 5750 significantly clarified responsibilities within all sectors. This view is shared by respondents at both 'middle' management and operative/technician level.

A total of five firms from across the industry did not believe that their QMS had clarified responsibilities. The responses of these firms is provided in case studies 10, 18, 20, 24 and 27.

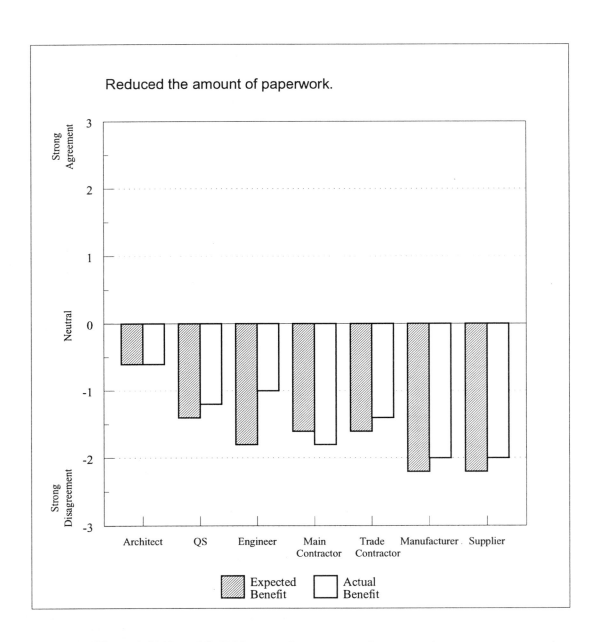

Figure 8 *Effect of QMS to BS 5750 upon the amount of paperwork*

Firms in all sectors clearly expected an increase in the amount of paperwork, and this proved to be the case. Four firms, namely those whose responses are given in case studies 01, 14, 25 and 31 felt that there had not been a significant increase in paperwork.

The experiences of the senior managers were generally endorsed by both 'middle' managers and operatives/technicians.

4.3.3 Costs

Three questions were used to examine the effect of the Standard in this area.

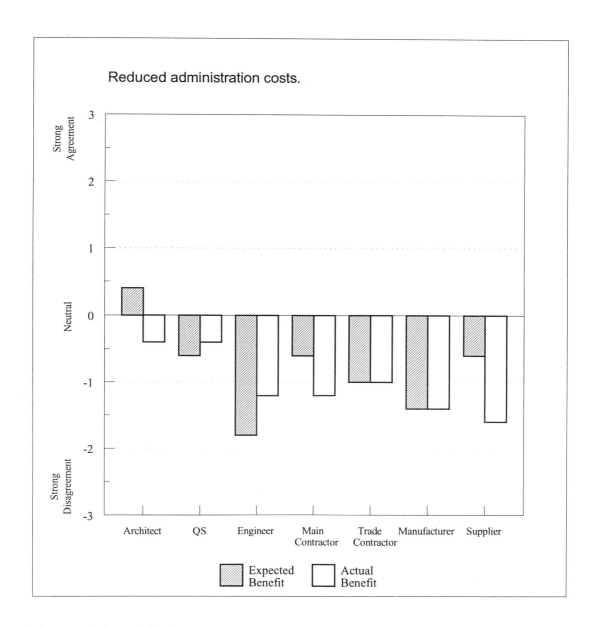

Figure 9 *Effect of QMS to BS 5750 upon administration costs*

Excepting the architects, most firms expected their administration costs to increase on implementing their QMS. Generally, experiences were in line with expectations, although five firms, namely those whose responses are shown in case studies 02, 06, 14, 25 and 31, were of the opinion that costs had been reduced. A further seven firms (case studies 26, 02, 06, 12, 16, 17 and 18) believed that their QMS had had little impact in this area. Three of these firms were main contractors.

The experiences of the senior managers were generally endorsed by both 'middle' managers and operatives/technicians.

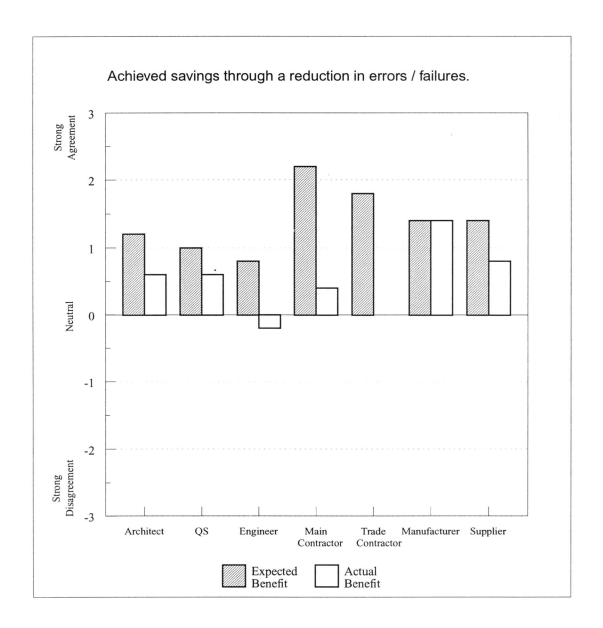

Figure 10 *Effect of QMS to BS 5750 upon incidence of errors*

Predictably, all of the firms anticipated a reduction in the level of errors. The expectations of main contractors and trade contractors were generally higher than those of other sectors.

Respondents from most sectors thought that there had been a significant reduction in errors through the implementation of their QMS. The average sector responses of the consulting engineers and main contractors shown in the graph should not be read as being representative. Two consulting engineers' responses were not available: of the remaining three firms two indicated that there had been a significant reduction in errors. Of the main contractors, only one firm (case study 20) reported that they had not made such improvements.

The responses from 'middle' managers and operatives/technicians indicated agreement with their senior managers. Those from the consulting engineers and quantity surveyors sectors believed improvements had been slightly higher than reported by senior managers. Main contractor operatives/technicians also thought improvements were greater than reported by their senior managers.

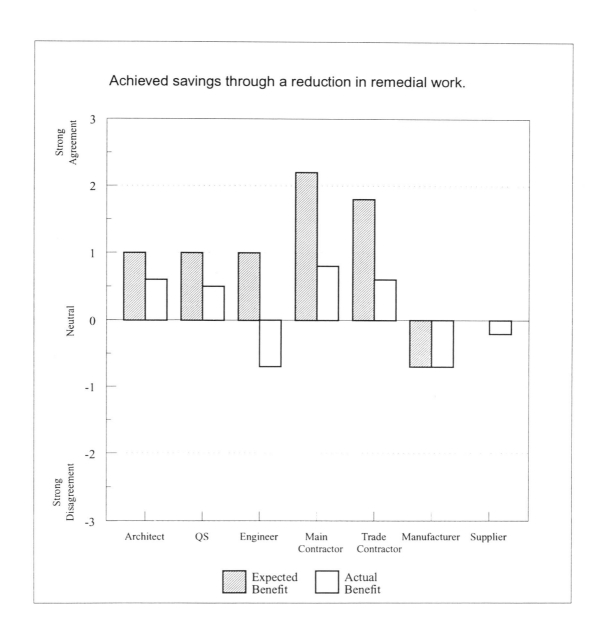

Figure 11 *Effect of QMS to BS 5750 upon the incidence of re-working*

With the exception of product manufacturers and material suppliers, firms expected to achieve significant savings through reduced remedial work. Generally, firms indicated that savings were made, although consulting engineers disagreed.

Responses from 'middle' managers and technicians/operatives from the consulting engineers sector concurred with the views of their senior managers. Material supplier respondents, however, believed that the level of savings made through reduced remedial work had been higher than reported by senior managers.

4.3.4 Planning and control

Four statements were used to examine the effect of the Standard in this area.

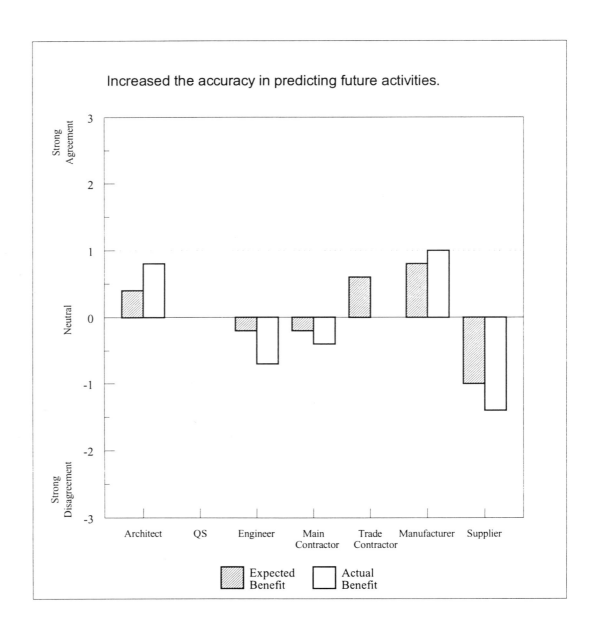

Figure 12 *Effect of QMS to BS 5750 upon accuracy of predictions*

The range in responses to this question is indicative of an uncertainty amongst respondents regarding the level of impact their QMS would have in this area. Generally, the benefits perceived were not significant and largely as expected. The views of 'middle' managers and technicians/operatives concurred with their senior managers' views.

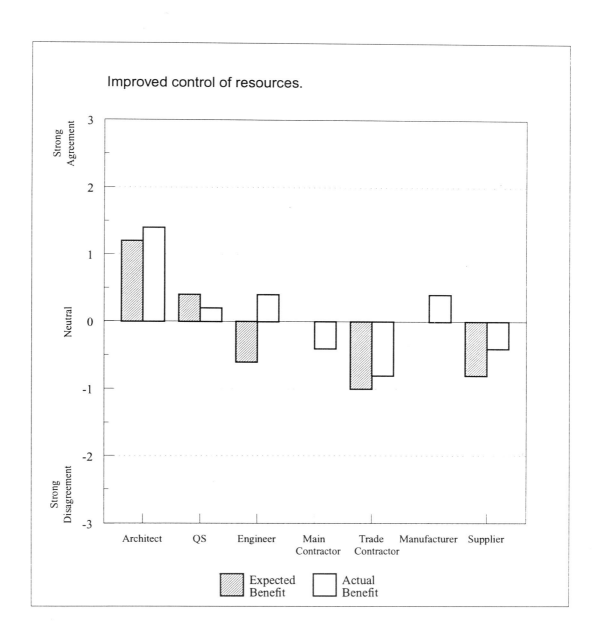

Figure 13 *Effect of QMS to BS 5750 upon control of resources*

Excepting the architects, no firms had any great expectations from BS 5750 regarding the control of resources within the firm and experience confirmed this. The architects, however, reported some improvements in this area.

Responses from 'middle' managers and operatives/technicians generally concurred with the views of their senior managers. Trade contractor, consulting engineer, main contractor and product manufacturer respondents, however, believed that the degree of control over resources within the firm had increased by more than reported by senior managers.

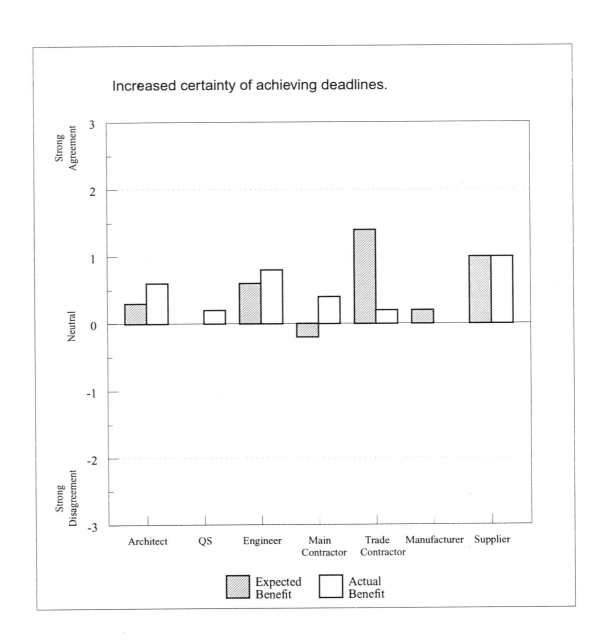

Figure 14 *Effect of QMS to BS 5750 upon achieving deadlines*

Most respondents, in particular trade contractors and material suppliers, reported that they had expected modest improvements in achieving deadlines. The graph shows that firms did believe that confidence had improved, but that the level of improvement had not been significant.

The views reported by senior managers were representative of all respondents interviewed.

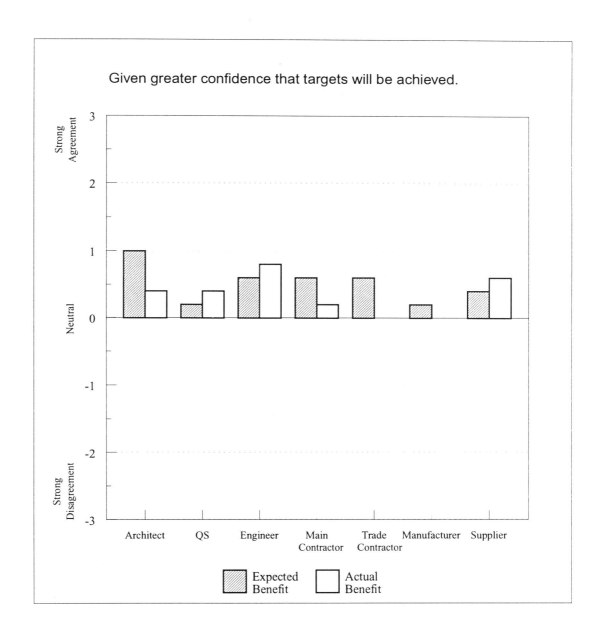

Figure 15 *Effect of QMS to BS 5750 upon achieving targets*

Firms from all sectors expected some improvements regarding confidence that targets would be achieved, although not by a significant amount. Broadly speaking, results gained were in line with expectations.

The views of 'middle' managers and operatives/technicians generally agreed with those of their senior colleagues. Operatives from the product manufacturing sector, however, had significantly higher expectations, which they believed were largely realised.

4.3.5 Morale

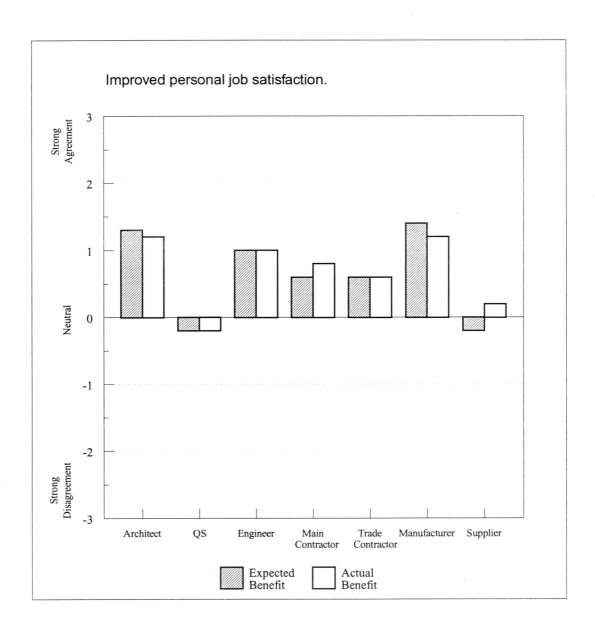

Figure 16 *Effect of QMS to BS 5750 upon job satisfaction*

Respondents had mixed expectations regarding the impact of their QMS upon their job satisfaction. Those from most sectors had expected job satisfaction to increase: Quantity surveyors and material suppliers, however, felt that any improvements would be overshadowed by the effects of the recession.

The benefits perceived by senior managers, which were representative of all the respondents interviewed, were very much in line with expectations.

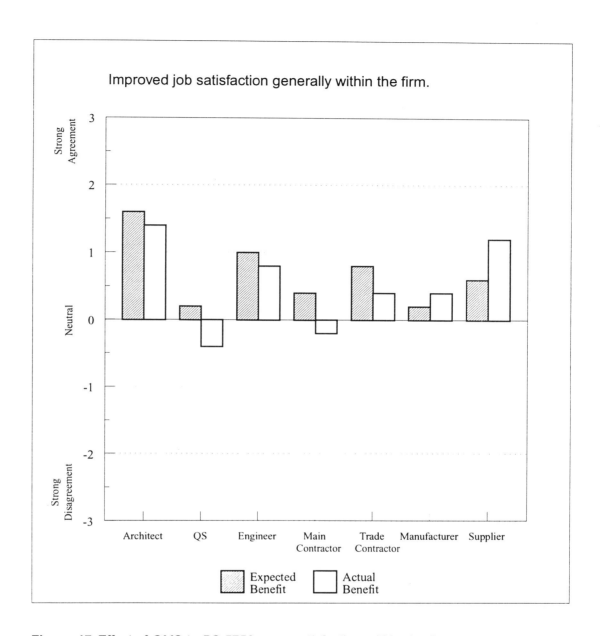

Figure 17 *Effect of QMS to BS 5750 upon satisfaction within the firm*

Expectations regarding the impact of their QMS upon satisfaction within the firm were mixed. Architects expected significant improvements, whilst respondents from other sectors were more modest.

Broadly speaking results were in line with expectations: one quantity surveyor (see case study 10) and two main contractors (case studies 19 and 20) felt that satisfaction had not increased significantly.

'Middle' managers and operatives/technicians generally held similar perceptions to their senior colleagues, although within firms of architects, expectations and perceived benefits were at a slightly lower level.

4.3.6 Management

Four questions were used to assess the impact of BS 5750 in this general area.

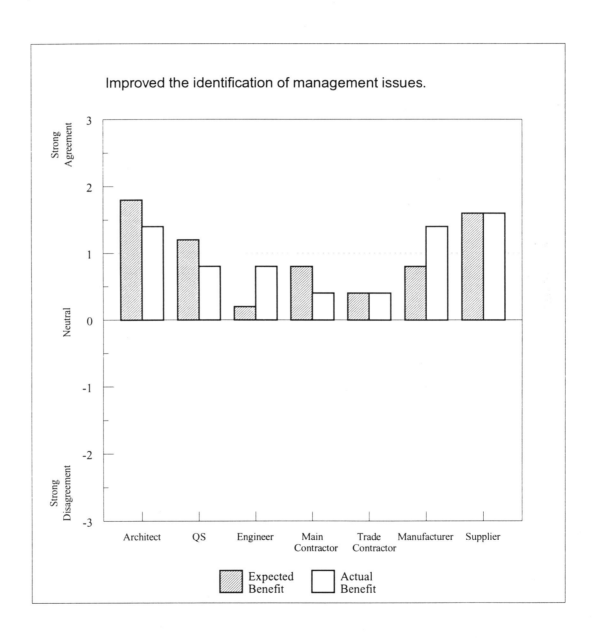

Figure 18 *Effect of QMS to BS 5750 upon identification of management issues*

All sectors indicated that the introduction of BS 5750 improved the identification of management issues.

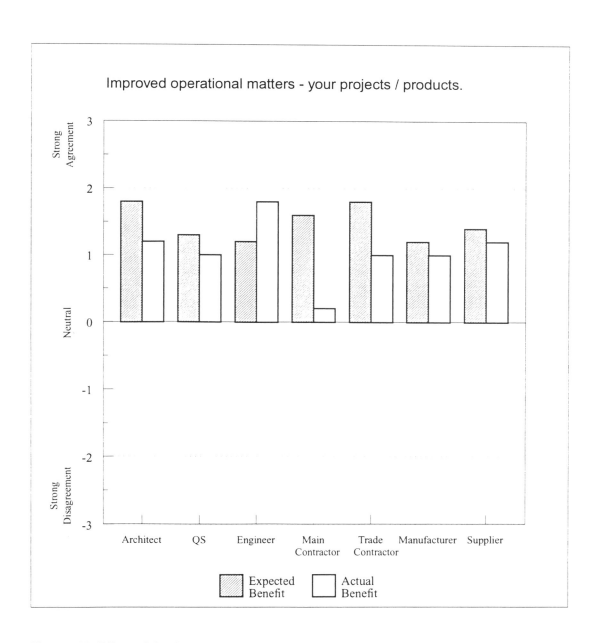

Figure 19 *Effect of QMS to BS 5750 upon improvements in products/services*

All firms expected their QMS to improve the products/services they offered. On the whole, some improvements were considered to be attributable to BS 5750. However, with the exception of the consulting engineers, actual improvements had not reached the level expected.

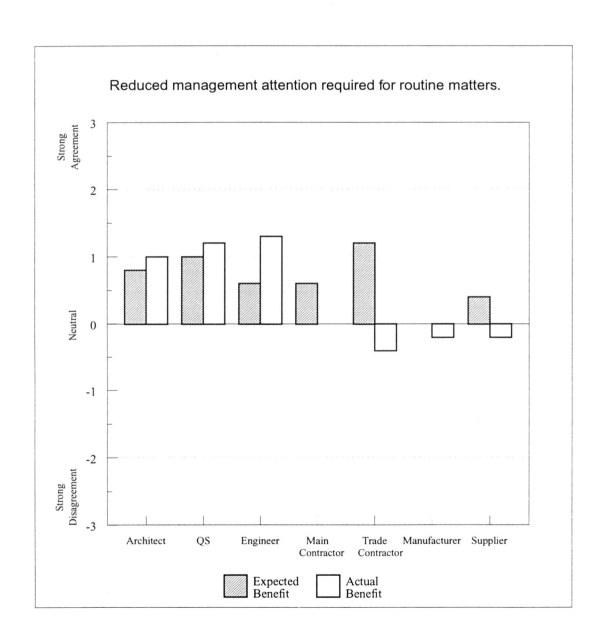

Figure 20 *Effect of QMS to BS 5750 upon the amount of time required for routine matters*

All professional services expected, and achieved, a significant reduction in the time required to deal with routine matters. The other sectors, however, reported that BS 5750 had little impact in this regard.

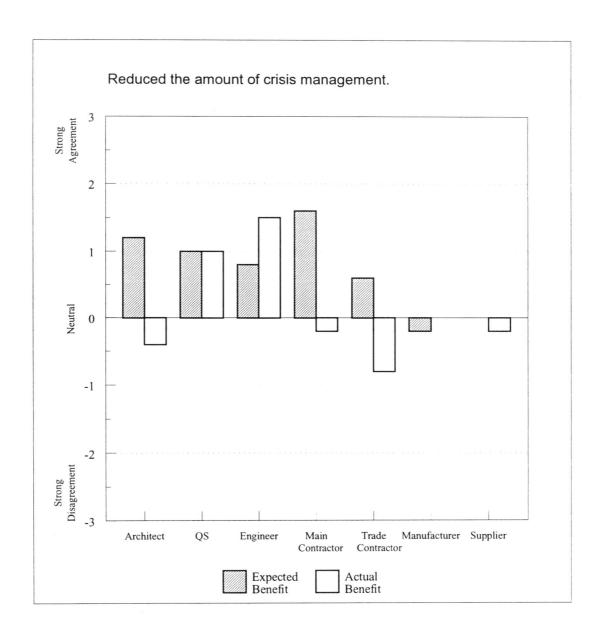

Figure 21 *Effect of QMS to BS 5750 upon the amount of crisis management*

Whilst the professional service firms and contractors had expected BS 5750 to reduce the degree of crisis management in their businesses, only the quantity surveyors and consulting engineers saw an improvement attributable to bs 5750. Firms operating in the remaining sectors had not reduced the amount of crisis management.

4.3.7 Customer/client relationships

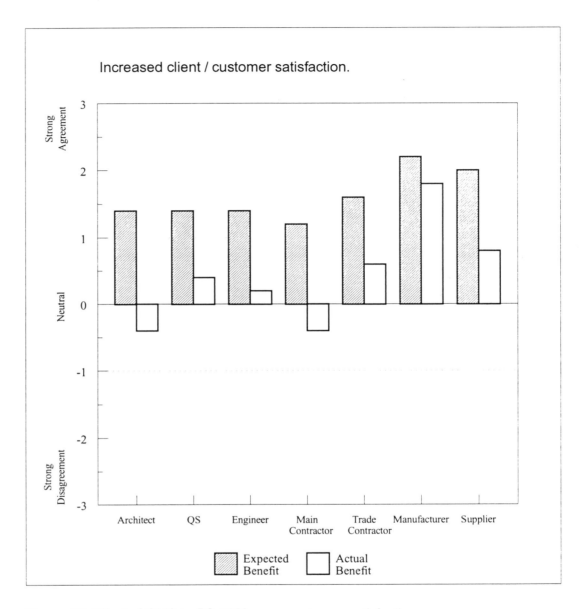

Figure 22 *Effect of QMS to BS 5750 upon customer satisfaction*

All firms had high expectations that BS 5750 would significantly increase the overall level of client satisfaction. With the exception of manufacturers, however, the increase in client satisfaction was significantly less than expected, particularly in the case of architects and main contractors. With regard to architects, middle and senior management both believed there had been no improvement in client satisfaction due to BS 5750 alone. Technicians, however, believed that there had been an improvement, broadly in line with expectations. Both main contractor middle management and operatives/technicians believed that client satisfaction had increased significantly, although not to the level expected. One particular main contractor felt strongly that other factors, such as location and price, had a greater impact on client satisfaction than quality. This explains the low overall response from this sector.

Section 5 deals with this subject area from the client's perspective.

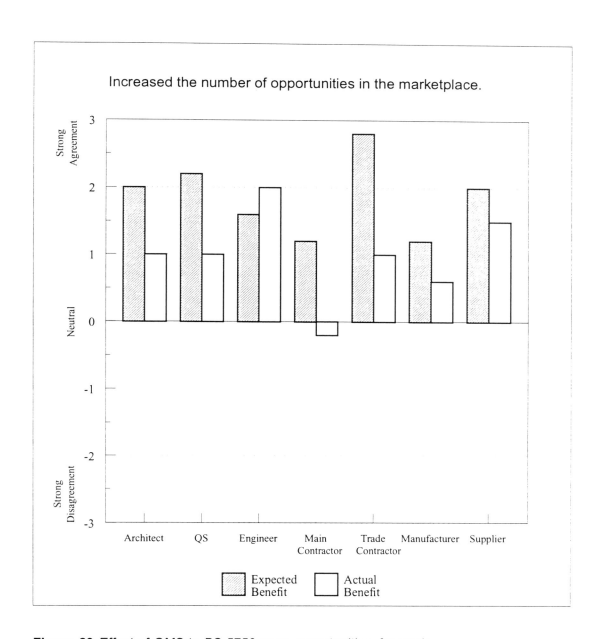

Figure 23 *Effect of QMS to BS 5750 upon opportunities for work*

All firms expected that certification would increase the level of business opportunities. With the exception of main contractors, firms believed that opportunities had increased, but not to the level expected. One senior manager interviewed, a main contractor operating primarily in the housing market, strongly disagreed that opportunities had increased as a result of gaining certification, believing that price has been a more important issue during the recession. In addition, one main contractor, certified only in 1992, reported that in his opinion it was still too early to ascertain whether certification was, to any extent, improving the level of enquiries. The remaining respondents from this sector believed that opportunities had increased broadly in line with expectations.

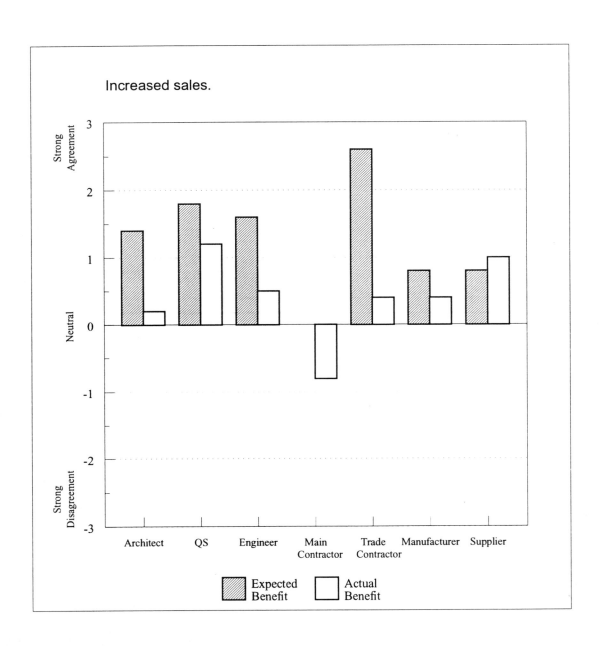

Figure 24 *Effect of QMS to BS 5750 upon sales*

All firms, except main contractors, expected BS 5750 certification to result in increased sales. Generally, sales had increased, but not to the degree expected. Main contractors, two of which had only recently been certified, had not expected (or attained) an increase in sales.

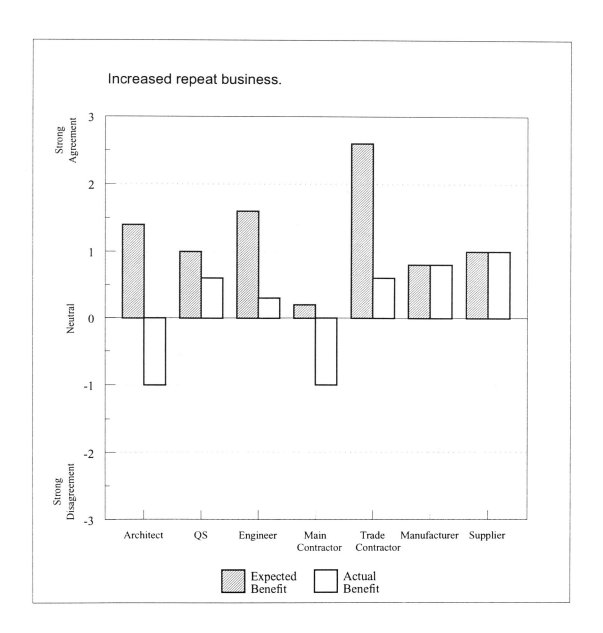

Figure 25 *Effect of QMS to BS 5750 upon repeat business*

Again, most firms expected and had gained an increase in repeat business, although not to the level hoped for. Due to a significant number of quantity surveyors and main contractors having only recently gained certification, the full benefits, in this regard, had not yet been realised.

4.4 OVERALL IMPRESSIONS OF THE EFFECT OF A QMS TO BS 5750 ON THE BUSINESS

Following discussions with respondents on their perceptions and expectations of a QMS to BS 5750 in specific key areas of the business, they were each asked to consider what overall effect operating their QMS to BS 5750 was having on the business as a whole, with particular regard to the quality of the products and services offered by their firm and the management of the firm.

Respondents were generally of the opinion that installing their QMS to BS 5750 and gaining certification had led to a significant improvement regarding both issues. Taking into account the responses of all senior managers, middle managers and operatives/technicians, the average perceived improvement regarding improvements to products and services offered by firms was in the order of 20%. The average level of improvement regarding management of the firm was 24%. All firms reported that, in their opinion, the implementation of their QMS had resulted in improvements: only four firms believed that their QMS had not improved their products and services, whilst four different firms had perceived no improvements to the management of their firm.

Whilst the overall level of improvement regarding both issues has been significant, the specific experiences of individual firms varied. Improvements regarding products and services ranged from 0% to 40% (reported by four firms), whilst those regarding the management of the firm ranged from 0% to 40% (reported by five firms). The individual firm's responses are provided in the case studies.

Most firms participating in this survey sought to improve the profile of their firm through improvements to the products and services supplied to their clients. The results of this survey indicate that the majority of firms had achieved significant improvements in this regard. They had also improved the management of their business.

4.4.1 Levels of overall improvement, by sector

The overall level of improvement reported by firms indicate that there are some variations between the seven business sectors:

Table 17 *Perceived levels of overall improvement*

	Improvements to products/services (%)	Improvements to management (%)
• Architects	22	24
• Quantity Surveyors	12	16
• Consulting Engineers	23	25
• Main Contractors	18	24
• Specialist and Trade Contractors	20	18
• Product Manufacturers	16	32
• Materials Suppliers	28	28

Many people believe that BS 5750 is more suited to manufacturing businesses than to those operating in the service sector. Whilst the figures above are based on only five firms within each sector, they indicate that operating a QMS to BS 5750 is perceived to provide significant levels of improvement in all the seven business sectors covered by this survey.

4.4.2 Summary of perceived benefits and drawbacks

The responses by firms regarding the impact of their QMS on key areas of the business, as shown throughout Section 4.3, indicate that the benefits perceived by firms have been greater in some areas of the business than in others. A summary is provided below of the main areas where significant improvements have been made, those where only small improvements have been perceived and those areas where respondents felt that performance had been adversely affected. Also included, are some of the illustrative comments made by respondents during the interviews.

The main areas of significant perceived benefit were:

- Company image

  'creates the impression of a club' (Architect)

  'increased our reputation within the industry' (Trade contractor)

  'sales have improved to companies which insist on QA'd supplies' (Supplier)

  'work gained from "high profile" clients' (Engineer)

  'people are more aware of how important it is to have products from a firm which carries the BS 5750 certificate. It is a guarantee that all systems are carried out under strict control' (Manufacturer)

- Improved information flow

  'has caused all relevant contract information to be more readily available' (Main contractor)

- Clarification of responsibilities

  'interfaces and responsibilities are defined in the management structure' (Trade contractor)

- Reduction in errors/failures

  'QMS was introduced...to reduce snagging...as part of original rationale for implementing QA' (Main contractor)

  'cost of appointing full-time QA manager off-set by savings through reduced remedial work, waste and delay' (Main contractor)

The main areas where only marginal benefit had been perceived were:

- Productivity

  'improved productivity because of clear operating procedures' (Quantity surveyor)

  'productivity has improved because of increased "right first time"' (Main contractor)

  'has focused more attention on the sites; away from head office' (Main contractor)

  'by implementing BS 5750, productivity has been improved to a certain extent, but it is the management who have control on how to improve on this by setting targets' (Manufacturer)

- Dealing with queries

  'complaints dealt with systematically' (Supplier)

  'easier to respond to queries, traceability' (Supplier)

- Savings through less remedial work

  'checking procedures identify errors before costs are incurred' (Trade contractor)

  'cost of appointing full-time QA manager off-set by savings through reduced remedial work, waste and delay' (Main contractor)

  'questionable' (Architect)

- Planning, control and confidence

  'no effect — still management dependent' (Architect)

- Job satisfaction within the firm

  'potential for TQM is enormous, 5750 provides a good framework' (Architect)

  'decreased morale through increased checking and hassle' (Trade contractor)

  'we can do more as a team by training men to do other jobs to achieve deadlines' (Manufacturer)

- Time required for routine matters

  'less management attention on day-to-day routines — so less supervision needed' (Architect)

  'more slick' (Supplier)

  'no hierarchy of importance of events; all matters require formal attention' (Architect)

- Amount of crisis management

  'has prompted and promoted discussion of issues which are not necessarily quality related' (Main contractor)

  'generally improved management awareness of problems' (Engineer)

- Client satisfaction

  'in general, clients are not bothered about BS 5750' (Quantity surveyor)

  'puts us on a level footing with manufacturers' (Supplier)

  'lack of feed-back; customer contact is at wrong level, e.g. clerk of works' (Main contractor)

  'better able to respond to customer needs, more quickly and with greater confidence' (Manufacturer)

- Sales and repeat business

  'some customers, e.g. councils will in future only purchase goods from BS 5750 certified firms' (Main contractor)

  'external factors prevalent, price dictates success!' (Trade contractor)

  'it will (provide more opportunities) but not yet' (Supplier).

The areas where performance had been adversely affected were:

Most firms believed that the amount of paperwork had increased and that administration costs had increased with it. Some firms, however, saw benefits as a result of an increase in administration control:

• Paperwork and administration costs

  'far too much' (paperwork) (Architect)

  'amount of paperwork has increased three times' (Manufacturer)

  'increased the amount of paperwork, for the better!' (Architect)

  'has caused all relevant contract information to be more readily available' (Main contractor).

4.5 CONCLUSIONS

The benefits which firms have gained as a result of implementing a QMS to BS 5750 have, overall, been significant, although the level of improvement has been significantly higher in some areas of the business than others. Furthermore, throughout the exercise, respondents stated repeatedly that the level of improvement, in most areas, had not lived up to expectation.

From the firms' experiences with BS 5750, the researchers conclude that there were three principal reasons why the level of benefit enjoyed by firms had not been as expected.

1. Whilst all the firms which participated in the survey did gain certification, there remains evidence that some firms still did not have a full understanding of BS 5750. The case studies provided in Part 2 of this report show those sections of BS 5750 which firms believed to be the least important to their business. Some firms, for example case studies 03, 04, 06, 09, 13 and 16, believed that Corrective Action, Inspection and Testing, Control of Nonconforming Product and Design Control were not important to their business; these sections of BS 5750 are, however, fundamental areas of the BS 5750 Standard.

2. Generally, the level of benefits expected from BS 5750 were, and in some cases possibly too high. In some areas of the business, such as image, definition of responsibilities and information flow, implementing a QMS to BS 5750 can be expected to yield significant improvements. It can also be expected to increase the level of paperwork and possibly increase administration costs accordingly. These attributes of BS 5750 have been generally experienced by the firms participating in this survey. In other areas, however, such as control over resources, job satisfaction, and planning and control, BS 5750 needs to be integrated with other management systems within the business in order to gain the maximum benefit. This may indicate that instead of viewing BS 5750 as a system which can be built upon and integrated with the overall management of the business, these firms had, to some extent, 'bolted' BS 5750 on to their business: this would explain why the level of benefits were lower than expected.

3. In Section 3 the manner in which firms carried out internal auditing and Management Review was discussed. A review of these processes suggests that many of the firms interviewed, whilst meeting the minimum requirements of BS 5750, had not enjoyed the full benefits that BS 5750 can bring. Evidence suggests that many were in danger of managing their QMS in a 'mechanical' manner. The investment that had been put into developing their people is acknowledged. They must ensure, however, that the development of their employees remains a priority. At the end of the day it will be the employees who improve the quality of the organisation, not BS 5750 alone.

5 Purchaser/client attitudes towards supplier and project quality

5.1 INTRODUCTION

One of the major objectives many firms sought to attain by installing a QMS to BS 5750 was to improve the profile of the firm and increase business opportunities. In this section the views of their clients are examined to ascertain what benefits they had received as a result of their suppliers gaining certification to BS 5750.

These clients represented a broad cross-section of the construction industry, as shown below:

Main contractors	7
Trade contractors	7
Public bodies	4
Manufacturers	3
Consultants	3
Materials suppliers	2
Retail/food industry	2
Public utility	1
Education	1

Two thirds of these clients themselves operated a formal QMS, and approximately half were BS 5750 certified.

5.2 CLIENT ATTITUDES AND REQUIREMENTS

5.2.1 The importance of supplier quality

The past few years have seen an increasing commitment by firms towards the quality of their products and services. This, in turn, has led to an expectation that their own suppliers should demonstrate a similar commitment to quality to ensure that their products and services meet requirements. Each of the 30 respondents who participated in the survey was asked to express their views regarding the importance of supplier quality.

Seventy percent of respondents stated that their suppliers must demonstrate a commitment to quality. The majority of firms believed that the quality of products or services provided by suppliers has a direct impact on the overall quality of their own products or services and, therefore, the relationship between supplier and customer is seen as being increasingly important: two thirds of the respondents claimed that they knew their suppliers well and had strong relationships with them. Only 10% indicated that this was not the case.

5.2.2 Supplier selection and BS 5750

The research set out to establish the importance of BS 5750 certification of a supplier, against other criteria, during the selection process. Whilst half of the firms stated that the achievement of certification was taken into account during the selection process, only five suggested that they had expected the firm to either have, or be working towards, BS 5750.

These views suggest that whilst attainment of BS 5750 certification is now a consideration in the selection process, other criteria, such as previous experience, are still considered to be more important.

5.2.3 The practical impact of BS 5750 on the client–supplier relationship

Of the 30 firms interviewed, some 24 confirmed that they had purchased products or services from their supplier both prior to and since their supplier's certification to BS 5750. Fifteen of these were able to state the approximate date of their supplier's certification.

Respondents were asked about the effects that certification of the supplier had had on their working relationship, in particular to assess what benefit (if any) their firms had received as a result. Questions and responses are summarised as follows:

Has the attainment of BS 5750 by your supplier:

1. Given you greater confidence that your requirements will be met?
   – 67% had increased confidence that their requirements would be met
2. Improved information flow between you and the supplier?
   – 40% were neutral
   – 40% said there was an improvement in the flow of information
3. Increased the efficiency in dealing with queries?
   – 40% were neutral
   – 43% said there was an improvement
4. Resulted in greater satisfaction?
   – 67% were now more satisfied
5. Resulted in an increase in opportunities for the supplier with your organisation?
   – 53% agreed that there was an increase in opportunities since BS 5750 certification
6. Resulted in an increase in repeat business with your organisation?
   – 40% agreed that an increase in repeat business was due to BS 5750 certification
7. Enhanced the supplier's overall image?
   – 87% indicated that there had been an enhancement of the supplier's image.
8. Increased the amount of paperwork received from the supplier?
   – 70% were in agreement with this statement.

The responses suggest that, overall:

- Clients received a significant improvement in the performance of their supplier following the supplier's certification to BS 5750.

- The level of improvement, in terms of confidence of meeting requirements, the time taken to deal with problems, and the overall image of the supplier, was greater in the opinion of the client than the supplier.

Respondents were also asked to consider whether the occurrence of faults had changed since the supplier had attained certification to BS 5750. The results are provided in Table 18:

Table 18 *Effect of QMS to BS 5750 upon common faults*

	Improved performance (%)	No change (%)	Poorer performance (%)
Materials	43	57	0
- defective products			
Design			
- misinterpretation of needs	33	67	0
- use of incorrect or out-of-date information	63	37	0
- misinterpretation of design standards	43	57	0
- poor communication with other designers	33	67	0
- production of an imprecise or inadequate specification	47	53	0
Construction			
- misinterpretation of drawings or specification	39	57	3
- poor communication with suppliers and subcontractors	43	50	7
- poor co-ordination of subcontracted work	33	67	0
- poor workmanship due to inadequate instructions	41	59	0
- inadequate site supervision	47	53	0

The results above indicate that the clients participating in the survey have seen a significant improvement in their suppliers' performance following their suppliers' certification to BS 5750. This is especially true regarding the proper use of design information.

5.3 THE IMPLICATIONS ON CONSTRUCTION PROJECTS

The 30 clients of the BS 5750 certified firms that participated in the survey were each asked to consider the practical impact of BS 5750 on construction projects. To assess this, their views were sought, firstly, on the importance of quality in construction, in relation to other considerations such as construction time and cost, and secondly, on the degree of improvement in key areas of the construction process.

Of the 30 respondents, 20 cited construction quality as being more important than either construction time or cost, and a further four commented that the subject of quality is becoming increasingly important in the construction process. Their views regarding the level of improvement in key areas of the construction process are given in Table 19.

Table 19 *Effect of BS 5750 upon construction projects*

	Improved performance (%)	No change (%)	Poorer performance (%)
Compliance with requirements	70	30	0
Construction time	30	67	3
Workmanship	50	50	0
Cost control	23	77	0
Working relationships	63	37	0
Communications	50	50	0

The results above indicate that in each area BS 5750 is thought by clients to have improved performance, especially in the areas of compliance with project requirements and working relationships.

5.4 PERCEIVED IMPORTANCE OF BS 5750, BY BUSINESS TYPE

The 30 respondents were asked to consider, for each of the seven types of business activity covered by this survey, whether they believed it important for such businesses to:

* operate a Quality Management System
* be certified to BS 5750.

Table 20 below summarises their responses.

Table 20 *Relative (sectoral) importance of QMS/Certification*

Type of business	High level of importance	
	Operate QMS (%)	BS 5750 Certified (%)
Architects	65	30
Quantity Surveyors	63	35
Consulting Engineers	84	63
Main Contractors	92	78
Specialist & Trade Contractors	88	70
Product Manufacturers	83	81
Material Suppliers	90	81

Table 20 indicates that the majority of purchasers believe a QMS is important for all of the seven types of business considered. The view that certification to BS 5750 is less important for professional organisations indicates that the standard is still, to a large extent, perceived as being primarily applicable to manufacturing businesses.

5.5 CONCLUSIONS

The experiences of clients of the firms participating in this survey suggest that certification to BS 5750 significantly improves supplier performance in key areas of the business, and can, therefore, be a successful tool in providing customer reassurance. It is interesting to note that the level of improvement was generally thought to be greater by clients than by the firms themselves.

This survey suggests that clients are taking an increasing interest in their suppliers' commitment to quality, especially those who are themselves certified to BS 5750, and that the supplier/client relationship is seen as an important one. Whilst BS 5750 is increasingly becoming a consideration in the selection process, there are other factors, such as previous experience, which are considered to be more important.

6 Other responses to market requirements for quality management

6.1 INTRODUCTION

Whilst BS 5750 may be the most well-known form of QMS, some firms decide, for various reasons, to adopt alternative strategies for quality management. This section of the report provides information regarding the experiences of such firms and compares these experiences with those of the BS 5750 certified firms participating in this survey.

Some 21 firms, believed to operate an alternative QMS to BS 5750, were approached regarding this survey. Only seven firms, covering all business sectors except Main Contractors, were prepared to participate in the survey.

6.2 OBJECTIVES

The firms who implemented an alternative QMS to BS 5750 were asked to state their objectives for quality within their organisations. The objectives stated were:

- to provide a high level of service quality to clients at 'market' prices

- to eliminate errors and reduce costs.

Broadly speaking, these objectives are similar to those of the firms certified to BS 5750 covered by this survey. The research set out to determine why these firms decided to adopt an alternative approach to BS 5750, how they went about it and the benefits that were gained.

6.3 METHODOLOGIES ADOPTED

All seven firms operating alternative approaches to quality management had considered BS 5750. In all cases except one, a conscious decision was made not to go down the BS 5750 route. One firm was intending to gain certification to BS 5750 in the near future.

The firms which participated in the survey represented two different approaches to the introduction of quality management. Five firms claimed to follow formal TQM programmes within their business whilst the remaining two dealt with the subject of quality within the day-to-day management of the business. The firm intending to gain BS 5750 certification had adopted the latter method.

Each respondent who completed a questionnaire was requested, where relevant, to explain why the firm had decided against the pursuit of BS 5750. The reasons given fall into a number of categories:

- BS 5750 is inappropriate to their business activities

- it involves too much paperwork

- it will be made obsolete by TQM

- knowledge of bad experiences encountered by others

- poor products/services received from their own BS 5750 certified suppliers.

One respondent forcefully expressed the following opinion about the role of management in the construction industry:

> *'Management's job is to manage its activities, and so first-party assessment is relevant. Third party certification in the construction context is an abrogation of management responsibilities. Quality must be built in to the construction process, it cannot be an add-on.'*

The senior managers who completed a questionnaire described some of the attributes they wished for in their own organisations:

- to develop our people and create a happy working environment with job security

- to develop a more motivated team

- to impress upon staff the importance of thinking quality rather than expecting it to be achieved by the application of rules.

Two conclusions can be drawn from these responses. Firstly, these firms perceived BS 5750 to be essentially an administrative system. Secondly, they believed that the most effective approach to quality management is through concentrating on the human development aspects of the business.

Despite their reservations towards BS 5750, these firms had, in fact, incorporated certain elements of the Standard within their own approach to quality management. These include the areas of:

- management responsibility

- purchasing

- process control

- internal auditing

- training.

These are key areas of BS 5750.

6.4 THE RESULTS CLAIMED

The respondents stated that a number of important improvements had been made to the business. These included:

> *'More harmonious office relationships'.*

> *'Improved staff morale'.*

> *'We have continued to improve our performance, i.e. the way we run our business, without distraction of bureaucratic documentation, and the cost of third-party certification.'*

> *'Very few design errors get through to construction. It has helped reduce time lost on poor concepts.'*

As a result of these improvements, the firms believe that improvements have been passed on to their clients, providing them with:

'Quality designs, refined and honed by the process of being challenged.'

'A reduction in the possibility of mistakes being made'.

Firms were asked to state how their 'alternative' approach compared to that of a competitor with BS 5750 certification. The following statements were made by the respondents:

'We know why and how we do things! It is people who produce the stronger [competitive] position, not just documentary systems!'

'TQM is a much more all-round approach to management, shared in, and fully understood by all staff rather than the sterile, strict paperwork approach of BS 5750, which can often be abused and resented by staff.'

'Negligible bureaucracy [very little paper] It [our system] concentrates on design concepts and harnesses peoples' talents. It adds value rather than simply checking that we have done what we said we were going to do.'

6.5 CONCLUSIONS

The firms which participated in this survey and operated an alternative quality management approach to BS 5750 fall into two categories: those who claimed to have designed their own quality management system and those who claimed to have adopted a formal TQM approach. In regard to the latter, the researchers have found very little evidence that a formal QMS – one that can be measured in a quantifiable manner – actually existed in these businesses. Indeed, one respondent stated his view on the subject of client pressure and BS 5750: '*We don't give in to threats.*'

Those firms who claimed to have designed their own system had, in fact, chosen to implement selected sections of the BS 5750 Standard. This suggests that either these firms see BS 5750 as a framework upon which other systems can be developed, or as an initial focus towards the introduction of quality management. Indeed, one of the firms participating in the survey stated it was their intention to seek BS 5750 certification at a later date.

The objectives of the TQM approach to quality management are essentially the same as those of the firms who have certified their businesses to BS 5750. The principal difference is that TQM is a far more people-orientated approach than BS 5750. It seeks to focus on the development of people and the processes they manage, rather than on the administrative aspects of a system for quality. Despite this difference in approach, these firms had, in fact, incorporated into their quality system a significant number of the areas addressed by BS 5750.

Many businesses which are not certified to BS 5750 claim to manage quality effectively. By not attaining certification, however, such businesses lose two important benefits that certification can bring. Firstly, by being certified to BS 5750, clients have independent assurance that the QMS is maintained to the standards required by BS 5750. Secondly, clients are able to understand the manner in which their suppliers manage quality. Those firms which had already made a significant investment, as high as £70,000 for one firm interviewed, may wish to reconsider the benefits of acquiring BS 5750 certification.

7 Conclusion

7.1 INTRODUCTION

Many thousands of firms have already achieved independent third-party certification to BS 5750. In carrying out the research for this study, the researchers were able to gain first-hand knowledge of the experiences of 35 such firms, from across the industry, with regard to their experiences of installing and maintaining a QMS to BS 5750, together with the impact this has had on their clients. The exercise was also able to draw on the practical experiences of a small number of firms who claim to have adopted alternative approaches to quality management. Throughout this process, the researchers have been able to both determine the experiences of those people interviewed and also form an overall impression regarding these experiences. In this final section of the report, a summary of the findings is provided, together with recommendations concerning the way forward for the industry.

7.2 OVERALL IMPRESSIONS OF BS 5750 IN THE CONSTRUCTION INDUSTRY

The measure of how effective a system is lies in the ability to meet its objectives. The results from this research exercise, as reported in Section 4, demonstrate that the firms from each of the seven sectors covered by the survey believed they had significantly improved both their products and services and the management of the business. These improvements in performance, endorsed by clients, demonstrate that operating a QMS to BS 5750 can be beneficial both to individual firms and to the construction industry as a whole.

These results, however, also pose a question. Why, then, is there so much debate on how appropriate BS 5750 is to the construction industry? To consider this issue one must go beyond the statistical analyses, and interpret the overall impressions gained throughout the exercise.

In broad terms, there are two basic approaches to implementing a QMS to BS 5750. The first is merely to follow the mechanics of ensuring that documentation and working practices meet the requirements of the Standard. The second is to examine how the business can best focus on the ever-changing opportunities in the marketplace and, through the development of people and the management of the individual business processes, develop a QMS which is primarily intended to satisfy the firm's objectives, but which also meets the requirements of the Standard. It is entirely feasible for both types of firm to gain certification and, in the opinions of the researchers, many firms end up — often unintentionally — with a QMS which identifies more closely with the first example than the second. The distinction between the two approaches is difficult to define as the main issue is one of culture. People either perceive their QMS as a system which must be adhered to, and which checks up on them (in other words a policing exercise), or as a tool placed in their hands to enable them to manage their work more effectively.

7.3 LESSONS TO BE LEARNED

The firms which participated in this survey have made significant improvements to their businesses and these improvements have been endorsed by their clients. However, a number of key issues have resulted from this survey which all indicate that further improvements could be made:

1. The report confirms that most firms had unreasonable expectations of what BS 5750 and certification can deliver. This is evident from the reports from interviewees which show that time and again actual experiences did not match expectations.

2. There still appeared to be some lack of understanding concerning the interpretation of BS 5750 in certain businesses. This is evident from the statements made by individuals regarding the areas of BS 5750 they saw as unimportant in their business.

3. The experiences of the firms participating in this survey suggest that significant improvements could be made regarding the development of their systems, through internal auditing and Management Review. Firms' experiences, as reported in Section 3, indicate that the scope of the review process could be extended to take account of all the areas affected by the QMS: it also indicates that firms may not fully understand how to develop their QMS in the most effective manner.

4. The experiences of firms with regard to second-party auditing by clients suggests that for some firms certification alone does not provide sufficient confidence that their quality requirements are met. This may suggest that some firms see BS 5750 as a basis on which to develop systems which go beyond the requirements of BS 5750, whilst other firms see BS 5750 as an isolated system.

The manner in which these firms designed, implemented and managed their quality management systems was presented in Sections 1, 2 and 3, in order to identify the lessons. In summary, any firm wishing to gain certification to BS 5750, or wishing to improve on an existing system, should consider the following issues:

Strategy: Define realistic and measurable objectives for quality. The firms participating in the survey generally had a clear understanding of what they wished to achieve.

Interpret the Standard's requirements for the business and consider whether expertise needs to be bought in. Most firms employed the services of a consultant to assist in this regard.

Consider which activities should be covered by the QMS — the scope.

Establish a strategy and budget for implementation of a QMS. Most firms did not, and relied on the consultant's advice regarding the most appropriate methodology. However, establishing a strategy and budget together with clearly defined objectives, as discussed in Section 1, should ensure that:

— the QMS can be designed and implemented quickly and efficiently

— all people in the business are involved and managed in the most effective manner

— there are yardsticks against which to measure progress

— the system designed is an effective one, and one which is 'owned' by the employees.

Design:	Management must demonstrate their commitment throughout the process and 'sell' the process to the employees. The QA Representative must have a voice in the management team.

Documentation should be developed with input from all employees involved. Again, this encourages ownership. Twenty-two of the 35 firms involved their employees in the development of the documentation.

Implementation: Manage the implementation process carefully. Don't let people believe they are being told to obey a set of rules.

Consider carefully which certification body to use.

Management: Train auditors well. Auditing should not be restricted to the identification of non-conformities but should provide input for relevant development. Firms' experiences in regard to the quality of auditing varied, with some gaining greater benefit than others. To achieve optimum results from their QMS, firms should ensure that auditors are well trained and managed.

Manage the review process carefully. Reviews will only be effective if quality of input data is high.

7.4 THE WAY FORWARD

Over the past few years, more and more firms have been persuaded to gain certification to BS 5750, especially those operating in the public sector. Unfortunately, this appears to be resulting in an increasing number of firms doing the minimum to gain certification. Whilst this process does result in improvements throughout the business, the levels attained are much lower than they could be.

For the industry to gain positive benefits from quality management in terms of efficiency and the quality of goods and services, a number of key issues should be considered:

1. Customers of the firms participating in this survey have confirmed that the relationship between supplier and customer is an important one. Whilst certification to BS 5750, as experienced by these firms, provides customers with reassurances that their supplier's quality management system conforms to the requirements of the Standard, the requirements of some customers may exceed those of BS 5750. Firms should, therefore, look to work more closely with their suppliers and take an active interest in their suppliers' quality management systems. Whilst this process may require investment in the short term, experience suggests, as seen in the automotive industry for example, that the payback in the longer term is advantageous. One method of ensuring that a supplier operates an effective QMS is to carry out a second-party audit, as described earlier in this report.

2. It is acknowledged that BSI have recently made significant revisions to BS 5750, now called BS EN ISO 9000. The additional requirements of the Standard should result in significant improvements in the way in which certified firms manage their QMS. However, BSI should perhaps consider publishing additional guidance notes to assist firms with the effective interpretation of the requirements of the Standard and to enable them to improve the manner in which they manage their QMS.

Many trade and professional bodies have developed codes of practice which interpret the standards requirements for their profession (see Bibliography), although some are relatively expensive. However, the Standard, the wording of which still has a strong bias towards manufacturing, could be made easier to interpret. The publication of guidance notes may help businesses improve their understanding of BS 5750.

In Section 6 the experiences of firms who claimed to have adopted a human development approach to quality using such systems as TQM and Investors in People were reported. These approaches actually complement BS 5750. Is there, perhaps, scope for the development of the Standard which combines both approaches in a structured way?

3. Over the last few years, there has been a rapid increase in third-party certification bodies and this trend is likely to continue. This has a number of implications. Competition between certification bodies may result in reduced fees and more focus being put towards the marketing of their services. These benefits are welcomed by the industry. The other less beneficial aspect is that in order to remain competitive the auditing process may become curtailed, and this gives cause for concern. The industry must look to the UKAS to ensure that certification bodies remain effective.

7.5 RESEARCHERS' FOOTNOTE

The research contractor has found this project to be both stimulating and revealing in that the extremes of enthusiasm, knowledge and commitment have been encountered when interviewing individuals. These extremes reflect directly on their organisation as a whole. Auditors and especially clients would, we believe, have similar impressions when visiting a number of BS 5750 certified suppliers.

It is recommended that further research work is conducted as to how clients, consultants and certification schemes can influence the development of a QMS to BS 5750 and beyond. At present the certification schemes do not differentiate between those organisations having a positive attitude and those who simply maintain their registration by merely correcting identified non-conformities.

Appendix 1 Phase 1 interviewees

Construction Industry Research and Information Association

Research Project RP455 (PROP1224)

Geographical Locations of Interviewees

A Architects
B Consulting Engineers
C Quantity Surveyors
D Main Contractors
E Specialist / Trade Contractors
F Material Manufacturers
G Material Suppliers

Figure 26 *Location of Phase 1 interviews*

Appendix 2 References to regulations included in QMS documentation

BUSINESS SECTOR	REGULATION
Architects	- Health and Safety on site - British Standards - Building Regulations - CISfB - IEE - PSA - CIBSE
Quantity Surveyors	- Health and Safety at work - British Standards - JCT Forms of Contract - Standard Method of Measurement - Pricing reference books
Consulting Engineers	- Health and Safety at work - British Standards - Codes of Practice - Building Regulations - CIBSE - IEE
Main Contractors	- Health and Safety at work - British Standards - Codes of Practice
Specialist and Trade Contractors	- British Standards - Health and Safety at work - Codes of Practice - NASC specifications - British Board of Agreement - British Property Federation

Construction Product Manufacturers	- British Standards
	- Codes of Practice
	- NAMAS
	- COSHH
	- HASAW

Construction Materials Suppliers	- British Standards
	- Health and Safety at work
	- COSHH

Appendix 3 Bibliography

BRITISH STANDARDS INSTITUTION
ISO 9000/BS 5750/EN 29000 *Quality Systems:*

BS 5750: Part 1: 1987 *Specification for design/development, production, installation and servicing*

BS 5750: Part 2: 1987 *Specification for production and installation*

BS 5750: Part 3: 1987 *Specification for final inspection and test*

BS 5750: Part 4: 1987 *Guide to the use of BS 5750: Part 1*

BS 5750: Part 8: 1991 *Guide to quality management and quality system elements for services*

BSI Standards Handbook 22, Quality Assurance

Quality Management in Construction − Certification of product quality and quality management systems
Ashford, J.L
CIRIA Publications, 1989

Oliver, B.M.
Quality Management in Construction − Interpretations of BS 5750 (1987), quality systems for the construction industry
CIRIA Special Publication 74, 1990

Barber, J.
Quality Management in Construction − Contractual aspects
CIRIA Special Publication 84, 1992

Oliver, B.M.
Quality Management in Construction − Implementation in design services organisations
CIRIA Special Publication 88, 1992

Grover, R. and Levers, A.
The impact of European Communities policy on quality management in construction
CIRIA Special Publication 89, 1993

Guidelines on BS 5750
Federation of Master Builders, 1993

Quality Assurance for Contractors
FCEC, 1988

Quality Assurance for Builders
BEC, 1988

Quality Manual and Procedures for Implementing BS 5750
FMB, 1993

Quality Management: Guidelines for an Office Manual
RIBA, 1990

Appendix 4 Sample case study

This sample case study is one of 35 presented in Project Report 32. The inclusion of this case study is mainly illustrative of the type and presentation in the Project Report 32. The figure should not, therefore be taken as being representative of the survey as a whole.

CASE STUDY NUMBER 13

BASIC INFORMATION ABOUT THE FIRM

Construction sector:	**Consulting engineers**	Number of employees:	**15**
Turnover:	**£1.4m**	Nr offices/plants:	**1**
Date of certification:	**February 1990**	Part of Standard:	**1**

THE FIRM'S OBJECTIVES FOR INTRODUCING A QMS

Objectives:

Increased efficiency − to increase profits by 10−30%

To become market leader (profile) and meet inevitable requirements from certain clients

Expected benefits:

Improved productivity and image

Increased opportunities, sales and repeat business (although much repeat business carried out prior to BS 5750)

THE DEVELOPMENT AND INTRODUCTION/IMPLEMENTATION OF THE QMS

Strategy for overall design of QMS:

Documentation introduced without input from staff; staff awareness sessions held

Feedback encouraged and procedures amended accordingly

Consultant assists with auditing

The documentation was prepared by:

QA Manager assisted by Consultant

Documentation was reviewed by:

As last item

The QMS includes reference to other activities, such as:

Personnel

The QMS represents a combination of pre and post Certification procedures in the following proportions:

Unamended	**80%**
Amended	**10%**
New	**10%**

CASE STUDY NUMBER 13

Phases and timescales of system development and implementation:

Key dates	Phase
1. First consideration of formal QA.......2. Starting work on system	1 month
2. Starting work on system...3. System applied to working processes	11 months
3. The system applied to working methods.....4. Date of certification	6 months
Total duration of development and implementation	<u>18</u>

The resources used to develop and implement the QMS:

Consultant: **not available**

Quality Manager: **15 weeks**

Staff time: **weeks (minimal)**

Certification fee: **not available**

The QMS covers the following activities of the company:

Design

Project management

Surveys and CAD facilities

The company also carries out the following business which is not covered by the QMS:

None

The QMS comprises the following documentation. The figures in brackets indicate the approximate number of pages in each:

Management and organisation (11)

Procedures (41)

Standard forms (36)

The position of the Quality Manager in the firm is:

Partner

The criteria considered in selecting the person for this position were:

Seniority

Experience

Knowledge of current procedures

CASE STUDY NUMBER 13

EXPERIENCES IN OPERATING A QMS

The resources invested annually to maintain the QMS:

Consultant: **£1000**

Quality Manager: **5 weeks**

Staff time: **5 weeks**

Certification fee: **not available**

The benefits obtained from carrying out audits:

Improvements have been introduced via auditing

Improved traceability of documentation confirmed

Difficulties arising out of the auditing process:

Time (compensated by benefits)

Items covered by the Management Review:

Procedures review

Systems review

Previous minutes of meetings

Quality records

The most important sections of BS 5750 in our opinion:

Management responsibility

Quality system

Contract review

Corrective action

Training

Design control

Document control

Control of non-conforming product

Internal quality system audits

The least important sections of BS 5750 in our opinion:

Inspection and testing

Inspection, measuring and test equipment

Inspection and test status

Quality records

(Others are considered not applicable)

BENEFITS OBTAINED FROM IMPLEMENTING A QMS TO THE REQUIREMENTS OF BS 5750 AND OVERALL SATISFACTION WITH THE PROCESS

Evaluation by Quality Manager (Partner) of the effects of implementing a QMS:

	Strongly agree						Strongly disagree
	3	2	1	0	(1)	(2)	(3)
1. Enhanced the firm's image	*						
2. Improved productivity throughout the firm				*			
3. Improved information flow			*				
4. Has reduced the time it takes to deal with queries			*				
5. Clarified responsibilities			*				
6. Reduced the amount of paperwork					*		
7. Resulted in a reduction of administration costs							*
8. Achieved savings through reduction in errors/failures							*
9. Achieved savings through a reduction in remedial work				*			
10. Greater accuracy in predicting future activities							*
11. Improved control of resources							*
12. Increased certainty of achieving deadlines			*				
13. Given greater confidence that targets will be achieved			*				
14. Improved my job description			*				
15. Improved satisfaction within the firm			*				
16. Improved the identification of management issues			*				
17. Improved operational matters		*					
18. Resulted in less management attention required for routine matters		*					
19. Resulted in a reduction in the amount of crisis management		*					
20. Resulted in greater client/customer satisfaction		*					
21. Resulted in greater number of opportunities	*						
22. Increased sales			*				
23. Resulted in an increase in repeat business				*			

The overall impression of the effects of our QMS:

- **the products/services offered**   **25% improvement**
- **the management of the firm**   **25% improvement**